Penguin Education
Voices The second book

Voices The second book

Also available

Voices The first book   **Voices** The third book
Voices Teachers' handbook

edited by Geoffrey Summerfield

With over 30 pages of illustrations

Penguin Books

For C.M.L. Con Amore

Penguin Books Ltd, Harmondsworth,
Middlesex, England
Penguin Books Australia Ltd, Ringwood,
Victoria, Australia

First published 1968
Reprinted 1968 (twice), 1969, 1970 (twice), 1971, 1972, 1973
This selection copyright © Geoffrey Summerfield, 1968

Printed in Hong Kong by
Sheck Wah Tong Printing Press
Set in Lumitype Baskerville

Contents

1 There Was a Man

There was a man with a tongue of wood
Who essayed to sing,
And in truth it was lamentable.
But there was one who heard
The clip-clapper of this tongue of wood
And knew what the man
Wished to sing,
And with that the singer was content.

STEPHEN CRANE

2 Madly Singing in the Mountains

There is no one among men that has not a special failing :
And my failing consists in writing verses.
I have broken away from the thousand ties of life :
But this infirmity still remains behind.
Each time that I look at a fine landscape,
Each time that I meet a loved friend,
I raise my voice and recite a stanza of poetry
And am glad as though a God had crossed my path.
Ever since the day I was banished to Hsün-yang
Half my time I have lived among the hills.
And often, when I have finished a new poem,
Alone I climb the road to the Eastern Rock.
I lean my body on the banks of white stone :
cinnamon I pull down with my hands a green cassia branch.
My mad singing startles the valleys and hills :
The apes and birds all come to peep.
Fearing to become a laughing-stock to the world,
I choose a place that is unfrequented by men.

PO CHÜ-I Translated from the Chinese by Arthur Waley

3 The Poets Agree to be Quiet by the Swamp

They hold their hands over their mouths
And stare at the stretch of water.
What can be said has been said before:
reeds Strokes of light like herons' legs in the cattails,
Mud underneath, frogs lying even deeper.
Therefore, the poets may keep quiet.
But the corners of their mouths grin past their hands.
They stick their elbows out into the evening,
Stoop, and begin the ancient croaking.

DAVID WAGONER

4 Subject Matter

No, I think a footsore sheep dog
obeying the weary whistle with a limp
or a close-up of gorse
lit with headlamps
leaning out all dusty at night
toward a brother thorn across the road;

or a stand of pine
lopped for firewood; yes, and a
solitary cabbage tree with its head blown off
a scraggy ruff of dead leaves
rattling at its neck. Not
these great chunks of landscape, Mount
Cook's fourteen guineas, rain on the
hills, south of this
and north of that. Please,
paint me a pub winder
with the din behind it.

W. HART-SMITH

5 Expression of Feelings, VII

Only be willing to search for poetry, and there will be poetry:
My soul, a tiny speck, is my tutor.
Evening sun and fragrant grass are common things,
But, with understanding, they can become glorious verse.

YÜAN MEI Translated from the Chinese by Robert Kotewall and Norman L. Smith

6   Blackberry-Picking
FOR PHILIP HOBSBAUM

Late August, given heavy rain and sun
For a full week, the blackberries would ripen.
At first, just one, a glossy purple clot
Among others, red, green, hard as a knot.
You ate that first one and its flesh was sweet
Like thickened wine : summer's blood was in it
Leaving stains upon the tongue and lust for
Picking. Then red ones inked up and that hunger
Sent us out with milk-cans, pea-tins, jam-pots
Where briars scratched and wet grass bleached our boots.
Round hayfields, cornfields and potato-drills
We trekked and picked until the cans were full,
Until the tinkling bottom had been covered
With green ones, and on top big dark blobs burned
Like a plate of eyes. Our hands were peppered
With thorn pricks, our palms sticky as Bluebeard's.

We hoarded the fresh berries in the byre.
But when the bath was filled we found a fur,
A rat-grey fungus, glutting on our cache.
The juice was stinking too. Once off the bush
The fruit fermented, the sweet flesh would turn sour.
I always felt like crying. It wasn't fair
That all the lovely canfuls smelt of rot.
Each year I hoped they'd keep, knew they would not.

SEAMUS HEANEY

7   'Out, Out –'

The buzz saw snarled and rattled in the yard
And made dust and dropped stove-length sticks of wood,
Sweet-scented stuff when the breeze drew across it.
And from there those that lifted eyes could count
Five mountain ranges one behind the other
Under the sunset far into Vermont.
And the saw snarled and rattled, snarled and rattled,
As it ran light, or had to bear a load.

And nothing happened: day was all but done.
Call it a day, I wish they might have said
To please the boy by giving him the half hour
That a boy counts so much when saved from work.
His sister stood beside them in her apron
To tell them 'Supper'. At the word, the saw,
As if to prove saws knew what supper meant,
Leaped out at the boy's hand, or seemed to leap –
He must have given the hand. However it was,
Neither refused the meeting. But the hand!
The boy's first outcry was a rueful laugh,
As he swung toward them holding up the hand
Half in appeal, but half as if to keep
The life from spilling. Then the boy saw all –
Since he was old enough to know, big boy
Doing a man's work, though a child at heart –
He saw all spoiled. 'Don't let him cut my hand off –
The doctor, when he comes. Don't let him, sister!'
So But the hand was gone already.
The doctor put him in the dark of ether.
He lay and puffed his lips out with his breath.
And then – the watcher at his pulse took fright.
No one believed. They listened at his heart.
Little – less – nothing! – and that ended it.
No more to build on there. And they, since they
Were not the one dead, turned to their affairs.

ROBERT FROST

8 Welsh Incident

'But that was nothing to what things came out
  From the sea-caves of Criccieth yonder.'
'What were they? Mermaids? dragons? ghosts?'
'Nothing at all of any things like that.'
'What were they, then?'
                            'All sorts of queer things,
Things never seen or heard or written about,
Very strange, un-Welsh, utterly peculiar
Things. Oh, solid enough they seemed to touch,
Had anyone dared it. Marvellous creation,

All various shapes and sizes, and no sizes,
All new, each perfectly unlike his neighbour,
Though all came moving slowly out together.'
'Describe just one of them.'
                                        'I am unable.'
'What were their colours?'
                                        'Mostly nameless colours,
Colours you'd like to see; but one was puce
Or perhaps more like crimson, but not purplish.
Some had no colour.'
                                        'Tell me, had they legs?'
'Not a leg nor foot among them that I saw.'
'But did these things come out in any order?
What o'clock was it? What was the day of the week?
Who else was present? How was the weather?'
'I was coming to that. It was half-past three
On Easter Tuesday last. The sun was shining.
The Harlech Silver Band played *Marchog Jesu*
On thirty-seven shimmering instruments,
Collecting for Caernarvon's (Fever) Hospital Fund.
The populations of Pwllheli, Criccieth,
Portmadoc, Borth, Tremadoc, Penrhyndeudraeth,
Were all assembled. Criccieth's mayor addressed them
First in good Welsh and then in fluent English,
Twisting his fingers in his chain of office,
Welcoming the things. They came out on the sand,
Not keeping time to the band, moving seaward
Silently at a snail's pace. But at last
The most odd, indescribable thing of all,
Which hardly one man there could see for wonder,
Did something recognizably a something.'
'Well, what?'
                        'It made a noise.'
                                        'A frightening noise?'
'No, no.'
                'A musical noise? A noise of scuffling?'
'No, but a very loud, respectable noise –
Like groaning to oneself on Sunday morning
In Chapel, close before the second psalm.'
'What did the mayor do?'
                                        'I was coming to that.'

ROBERT GRAVES

12

9 The Nightmare

One night, about the time I came of age, I dreamt that
demon creatures fought with me while I slept . . . When I
woke I told this vision in verse, that the dreamers of
posterity might use my poem as a spell to drive off evil
dreams. And so often has it proved its worth that I dare
not any longer hide it from the world. The words are these:

Once, as in the darkness I lay asleep by night,
Strange things suddenly saw I in my dream;
All my dream was of monsters that came about me while I
    slept,
Devils and demons, four-horned, serpent-necked,
Fishes with bird-tails, three-legged bogies
From six eyes staring; dragons hideous,
Yet three-part human.
On rushed the foul flocks, grisly legions,
Stood round me, stretched out their arms,
Danced their hands about me, and sought to snatch me from
    my bed.
Then I cried (and in my dream
My voice was thick with anger and my words all awry),
'Ill-spawned elves, how dare you
Beset with your dire shapes Creation's cleanest
Shapeliest creature, Man?' Then straightway I struck out,
Flashed my fists like lightning among them, thumped like
    thunder,
Here slit Jack-o -Lantern,
Here smashed fierce Hog-Face,
Battered wights and goblins,
Smote venturous vampires, pounded in the dust
Imps, gnomes and lobs,   — clumsy fellows
Kobolds and kelpies;   — goblins | water demons
Swiped bulge-eyed bogies, oafs and elves;
Clove Tough-head's triple skull, threw down
Clutching Night-hag, flogged the gawky Ear-wig Fiend
That floundered toward me on its tail.

I struck at staring eyes,
Stamped on upturned faces; through close ranks

Of hoofs I cut my way, buried my fingers deep
In half-formed flesh;
Ghouls tore at my touch; I slit sharp noses,
Trod on red tongues, seized shaggy manes,
Shook bald-heads by the beard.
Then was a scuffling. Arms and legs together
Chasing, crashing and sliding; a helter-skelter
Of feet lost and found in the tugging and toppling,
Cuffing, cudgelling, frenzied flogging . . .

So fought I, till terror and dismay
Shook those foul flocks; panic spread like a flame
Down mutinous ranks; they stand, they falter,
Those ghastly legions; but fleeing, suddenly turn
Glazed eyes upon me, to see how now I fare.
At last, to end their treachery
Again I rushed upon them, braved their slaver and snares,
Stood on a high place, and lashed down among them,
Shrieking and cursing as my blows crashed.
Then three by three and four by four
One after another hop-a-trot they fled,
Bellowing and bawling till the air was full of their breath –
Grumbling and snarling,
Those vanquished ogres, demons discomfited,
Some that would fain have run
Lolling and lurching, some that for cramped limbs
Could not stir from where they stood. Some over belly-wounds
Bent double; some in agony gasping and groaning.
Suddenly the clouds broke and (I knew not why)
A thin light filtered the darkness; then, while again
I sighed in wonder that those disastrous creatures,
Dire monstrosities, should dare assail
A clean and comely man, . . . there sounded in my ears
A twittering and crowing. And outdoors it was light.
The noisy cock, mindful that dawn was in the sky,
Had crowed his warning, and the startled ghosts,
Because they heard dawn heralded, had fled
In terror and tribulation from the rising day.

(In an epilogue the poet seeks consolation in the fact that
many evil dreams and occurrences have in the past been

omens of good. Duke Huan of Ch'i, while hunting in the marshes, saw in a vision an ogre 'as broad as a cartwheel and as long as a shaft, wearing a purple coat and red cap'. It was an omen that he would rise to the Pentarchy. Wu Ting, Emperor of the Shang dynasty, was haunted in a dream by the face of the man who afterwards became his wise counsellor and friend. Wên, Duke of Chin, dreamt that the Marquis of Ch'u held him prostrate and sucked out his brains; yet his kingdom defeated Ch'u. Lao Tzŭ made use of demons, and thereby became leader among the Spirits of Heaven. 'So evil turns to good.')

WANG YEN-SHOU Translated from the Chinese by Arthur Waley

10 A Winter Scene

The noses are running at our house.

taps Like faucets. Wild horses.
Otherwise it is quiet here;
There is nothing afoot except Lassie who is running
Hastily through a TV pasture in quest of a
TV doctor, while we
Who are not running (except for our noses)
Vegetate (off TV) with Vicks and prescriptions
In an atmosphere so sedentary that if
We ever get well and get up and regain the potential
For running again with more than just our noses,
We may not.
            I mean it is possible
That when we get well we will not undertake to run
Or even to walk (though we'll be able to),
But will hold firm to our sofas and spread our Vicks
Ever more thickly over our throats and chests, letting Lassie
And such other TV characters as may follow
On Channel Five
Do all our running, walking, barking, thinking
For us, once even our noses
Have stopped their incessant running and it is quiet here.

REED WHITTEMORE

11 A Fire-Truck

Right down the shocked street with a siren-blast
That sends all else skittering to the curb,
Redness, brass, ladders and hats hurl past,
    Blurring to sheer verb,

Shift at the corner into uproarious gear
And make it around the turn in a squall of traction,
The headlong bell maintaining sure and clear,
    Thought is degraded action!

Beautiful, heavy, unweary, loud, obvious thing!
I stand here purged of nuance, my mind a blank.
All I was brooding upon has taken wing,
    And I have you to thank.

As you howl beyond hearing I carry you into my mind,
Ladders and brass and all, there to admire
Your phoenix-red simplicity, enshrined
    In that not extinguished fire.

RICHARD WILBUR

12 Gunpowder Plot

For days these curious cardboard buds have lain
In brightly coloured boxes. Soon the night
Will come. We pray there'll be no sullen rain
To make these magic orchids flame less bright.

Now in the garden's darkness they begin
To flower: the frenzied whizz of Catherine-wheel
Puts forth its fiery petals and the thin
Rocket soars to burst upon the steel

Bulwark of a cloud. And then the guy,
Absurdly human phoenix, is again
Gulped by greedy flames: the harvest sky
Is flecked with threshed and glittering golden grain.

'Uncle! A cannon! Watch me as I light it!'
The women helter-skelter, squealing high,
Retreat; the paper fuse is quickly lit,
A cat-like hiss, and spit of fire, a sly

Falter, then the air is shocked with blast.
The cannon bangs and in my nostrils drifts
A bitter scent that brings the lurking past
Lurching to my side. The present shifts,

Allows a ten-year memory to walk
Unhindered now; and so I'm forced to hear
The banshee howl of mortar and the talk
Of men who died, am forced to taste my fear.

I listen for a moment to the guns,
The torn earth's grunts, recalling how I prayed.
The past retreats. I hear a corpse's sons –
'Who's scared of bangers!' 'Uncle! John's afraid!'

VERNON SCANNELL

13 Guy Fawkes' Day

I am the caught, the cooked, the candled man
With flames for fingers and whose thin eyes fountain,
I send on the stiff air my shooting stare
And at my shoulder bear the burning mountain.

I open on the dark my wound of speeches,
With stabs, with stars its seven last words wear,
My tongue of torches with the salamander
Breeds conversaziones of despair.

Milled in the minted light my skin of silver
Now curls, now kindles on the thicket's bone,
And fired with flesh in sepulchres of slumber
Walks the white night with sparks and showers sown.

At my fixed feet soldiers my coat of carbon
Slit with the speared sky. Their sacked eyes scan
My mask of medals. In bright mirrors of breath
Our faces fuse in death. My name is man.

CHARLES CAUSLEY

14 At a Country Fair

At a bygone Western country fair
I saw a giant led by a dwarf
With a red string like a long thin scarf;
How much he was the stronger there
    The giant seemed unaware.

And then I saw that the giant was blind,
And the dwarf a shrewd-eyed little thing;
The giant, mild, timid, obeyed the string
As if he had no independent mind,
    Or will of any kind.

Wherever the dwarf decided to go
At his heels the other trotted meekly,
(Perhaps – I know not – reproaching weakly)
Like one Fate bade that it must be so,
    Whether he wished or no.

Various sights in various climes
I have seen, and more I may see yet,
But that sight never shall I forget,
And have thought it the sorriest of pantomimes,
    If once, a hundred times!

THOMAS HARDY

15 Bartleme Fair

Bartholomew

While gentlefolks strut in their silver and satins,
We poor folks that tramp it in straw hats and pattens,
As merrily old English ballads can sing-o,
operas' As they in their opperores' outlandish lingo ;
Calling out, bravo, encoro, and caro,
Though I will sing nothing but Bartleme Fair-o.

Here first of all, crowds against other crowds driving,
Like wind and tide meeting, each contrary striving ;
Here's fiddling and fluting, and shouting and shrieking,
Fife's trumpets, drums, bag-pipes, and barrow-girls squeaking ;
My ware round and sound, here's a choice of fine ware-o,
Though all is not sound bought at Bartleme Fair-o.

Here are drolls, hornpipe dancing, and showing of postures ;
Plum-porridge, black puddings, and op'ning of oysters ;
The tap-house guests swearing, and gall'ry folks squalling,
With salt-boxes, solos, and mouth-pieces bawling ;
Pimps, pick-pockets, strollers, fat landladies, sailors,
Bawds, bullies, jilts, jockies, thieves, tumblers, and tailors.

Here's Punch's whole play of the gunpowder-plot, Sir,
Wild beasts all alive, and pease-porridge hot, Sir :
Fine sausages fried, and the Black on the wire ;
The whole court of France, and nice pig at the fire.
The ups-and-downs, who'll take a seat in the chair-o ?
There are more ups-and-downs than at Bartleme Fair-o.

Here's Whittington's cat, and the tall dromedary,
The chaise without horses, and Queen of Hungary ;
The merry-go-rounds, come who rides ? come who rides ?
Wine, beer, ale, and cakes, fire-eating besides ;
The famed learnèd dog that can tell all his letters,
And some men, as scholars, are not much his betters.

This world's a wide fair, where we ramble 'mong gay things ;
Our passions, like children, are tempted by play-things ;
By sound and by show, by trash and by trumpery,
The fal-lals of fashion, and Frenchified frumpery.
Life is but a droll, rather wretched than rare-o,
And thus ends the ballad of Bartleme Fair-o.

GEORGE ALEXANDER STEVENS

16 Term Time

There's some that sing of the hiring fair
And sound out an alarm,
But the best old song that ever was sung
It is about the term.
The term time it is drawing near.
When we will all win free,
And with the hungry farmers
Again will never fee.

With broadtail coats and Quaker hats,
And whips below their arms,
They'll hawk and call the country round
A-seeking for their farms,
And they'll go on some twenty mile
Where people doesn't know 'em,
And there they'll hire their harvest hands,
And bring them far from home.

They'll tip you on the shoulder
And ask if you're to fee,
They'll tell you a fine story
That's every word a lie;
They'll tell you a fine story
And get you to perform
But, lads, when you are under them
It's like a raging storm.

On cabbage cold and taters
They'll feed you like the pigs
While they sit at their tea and toast,
And ride about in gigs.
The mistress must be 'Ma'am' and you
Must lift your cap to her;
And before you find an entrance
The master must get 'Sir'.

The harvest time when it comes round
They'll grudge you sabbath rest.
They'll let you to the worship,
But they like the working best.
The dinner hour it vexes them
And then to us they'll say,
'Come on, my lads, you'll get your rest
When lying in the clay.'

TRADITIONAL

17 Times Change

Man to the plough,
Wife sow,
Boy flail,
Girl pail,
And your rents will be netted.
But man, tallyho!
Miss, piano,
Boy, Greek and Latin,
Wife, silk and satin,
And you'll soon be gazetted.

TRADITIONAL

18 Not for Joseph

Joseph Baxter is my name,
    My friends all call me Joe.
I'm up, you know, to every game,
    And everything I know.
Ah, I was green as green could be,
    I suffered for it, though:
Now, if they try it on with me,
    I tell them not·for Joe.

Not for Joe, not for Joe,
If he knows it, not for Joseph,
    No, no, no,
    Not for Joe,
Not for Joseph, Oh dear no!

ANONYMOUS

19 The Keeper of the Nore

My father he kept the Eddystone light
And he married a mer-mi-ade one night,
On account of which he had offspring three –
Two of them were fish and t'other was me.
When I was but a bit of a chip
I was put in charge of the Nore lightship:
I kept my lamps in very good style,
A-doing of the work according to Hoyle.

Oh the rolling Nore, the raging Nore,
The waves they tumble o'er and o'er;
There's no such life to be had on shore,
Like the life that is led by the man on the Nore.

lantern One night as I was a-trimming of the glim,
A-singing a verse of the evening hymn,
I saw by the light of my signal lamp
The form of my mother looking awfully damp:
Just then a voice cries out 'Ahoy!'
And there she was a-sitting on a buoy –
That's a-meaning a buoy for the ships that sail,
And not a boy that's a juvenile male.

Says I to me mother, 'Now how do yer do?
And how's my father and my sisters two?'
Says she, 'It's an orph-i-an you are,
For you've only one sister, and you've got no pa.
Your father was drowned with several pals
And digested by the cannibals:
Of your sisters, one was cooked in a dish,
And t'other one is kept as a talking fish.'

At that I wept like a soft-eyed scamp –
My tears they made the water damp ;
Says I to my mother, 'Won't you step within –
You look so wet – just to dry your skin ?'
Says she, 'I likes the wet, my dear.'
Says I, 'Let me offer you the cabin chair.'
My mother, she looks at me with a frown,
'It's owing to my nature that I can't sit down.'

Says my mother, 'Now never you go on shore,
But always remain the man at the Nore.'
At that I saw a glittering scale,
And that was the end of my mother's tale.
Now, in deference to that maternal wish,
I can't visit my sister, the talking fish.
If you happen to see her when you go on shore,
Just give her the respects of the Man at the Nore.

TRADITIONAL

20 I'll Have the Whetstone

Hey, hey, hey, hey!
I'll have the whetstone if I may.

pickling pork   I saw a dog soaking sowse,
And an ape thatching a house,
And a pudding eating a mouse.
     I'll have the whetstone if I may.

cut out cloth   I saw a hedgehog shape and sew,
And another bake and brew,
Scour the pots till they looked like new.
     I'll have the whetstone if I may.

I saw a codfish corn sow,
And a worm a whistle blow,
And a magpie pummel a crow.
     I'll have the whetstone if I may.

I saw a kipper drag a harrow,
And yet another push a barrow,
And a herring shoot an arrow.
  I'll have the whetstone if I may.

I saw a wild pig faggots bind,
And a frog wool-skeins unwind,
And a toad fine mustard grind.
  I'll have the whetstone if I may.

weave I saw a sow bear kerchiefs to wash;
The second had a hedge to plash;
The third went to the barn to thrash.
  I'll have the whetstone if I may.

I saw an egg scoffing a pie.
Give me drink, my mouth is dry!
It's no time since I told a lie.
  I'll have the whetstone if I may.

ANONYMOUS

21 The Dragon of Wantley

Old stories tell how Hercules
A dragon slew at Lerna,
With seven heads, and fourteen eyes
To see and well discern-a:
But he had a club, this dragon to drub,
Or he'd never have done it, I warrant ye:
But More of More-Hall, with nothing at all,
He slew the dragon of Wantley.

This dragon had two furious wings,
Each one upon each shoulder;
With a sting in his tail as long as a flail
Which made him bolder and bolder.
He had long claws, and in his jaws
Four and forty teeth of iron;
buffalo   With a hide as tough as any buff
Which did him round environ.

Have you not heard how the Trojan horse
Held seventy men in his belly?
This dragon wasn't quite so big
But very near, I'll tell ye.
Devoured he poor children three
That could not with him grapple,
And at one sup he ate them up,
As you would eat an apple.

All sorts of cattle this dragon did eat,
Some say he ate up trees,
And that the forests sure he would
Devour by degrees:
For houses and churches were to him geese and turkies;
He ate all, and left none behind,
But some stones, dear Jack, that he couldn't crack,
Which on the hills you'll find.

In Yorkshire, near fair Rotherham,
The place I know it well;
Some two or three miles, or thereabouts,
I vow I cannot tell;

But there is a hedge, just on the hill edge,
And Matthew's house hard by it;
O there and then was this dragon's den,
You could not choose but spy it.

Some say this dragon was a witch,
Some say he was a devil;
For from his nose a smoke arose,
And with it burning snivel,
Which he cast off, when he did cough,
In a well that he did stand by;
Which made it look just like a brook
Running with burning brandy.

Hard by, a furious knight there dwelt
Of whom all towns did ring;
For he could wrestle, play at quarter-staff, cuff and huff,
Call people rude names, do any kind of thing:
By the tail and the mane, with his hands twain,
He swung a horse till he was dead;
And what is still stranger, for very anger
He ate him all up but his head.

These children, as I told, being eat,
Men, women, girls and boys,
Sighing and sobbing, came to his lodging,
And made a hideous noise:
'O save us all, More of More-Hall,
Thou peerless knight of these woods;
Do but slay this dragon, who won't leave us a rag on,
And we'll give thee all our goods.'

'Tut, tut,' quoth he, 'no goods I want;
But I want, I want, in sooth,
A fair maid of sixteen, both brisk and keen,
With smiles about the mouth;
Hair black as sloe, skin white as snow,
With blushes her cheeks adorning;
To anoint me o'er the night, ere I go to fight,
And to dress me in the morning.'

This being done, he did engage
To hew the dragon down;
But first he went, new armour to
Bespeak at Sheffield town,
With spikes all about, not within but without,
Of steel so sharp and strong.
Both behind and before, arms, legs, and all o'er
Some five or six inches long.

Had you but seen him in this dress,
How fierce he looked and how big,
You would have thought him to be
Some Egyptian porcupig.
He frighted all, cats, dogs, and all,
Each cow, each horse, and each hog:
For fear they did flee, for they took him to be
Some strange outlandish hedge-hog.

To see this fight, all people then
Got up on trees and houses,
On churches some, and chimneys too,
But these put on their trowses
So's not to spoil their hose. As soon as he rose
To make him strong and mighty,
He drank, by the tale, six pots of ale,
spirits And a quart of aqua-vitae.

It is not strength that always wins,
For wits do strength excel;
Which made our clever champion
Creep down into a well,
Where he did think this dragon would drink,
And so he did in truth;
And as he stooped low, he leapt up and cried 'Boh!'
And hit him in the mouth.

'Oh!' cried the dragon. 'Plague on thee, come out!
Thou disturb'st me in my drink.'
And then he turned, and shot at him,
Good grief, how he did stink!

'Beshrew thy soul, thy body's foul,
Thy dung smells not like balsam :
Thou blackamore, thou stink'st so sore,
Sure thy diet is unwholewome.'

Our clever old knight, on the other side,
Crept out upon the brink,
And gave the dragon such a douse
He knew not what to think.
'By cock!' quoth he, 'say you so? Do you see?'
And then at him let fly
With hand and with foot, and so they went to it,
And the word it was, 'Hey, boys, hey!'

'Your words,' quoth the dragon, 'I don't understand.'
Then to it they fell one and all,
Like two wild boars so fierce, if I may
Compare great things with small.
Two days and a night, with this dragon did fight
Our champion on the ground ;
Tho' their strength it was great, their skill it was neat ;
They never had one wound.

At length the hard earth began to quake,
The dragon gave him a knock
Which made him to reel, and straightway he thought
To lift him as high as a rock
And then let him fall. But More of More-Hall,
Like a valiant son of Vulcan,
As he came like a lout, so he turned him about
And hit him a kick on the bottom.

'Oh,' quoth the dragon, with a deep sigh,
And turned six times together,
Sobbing and tearing, cursing and swearing
Out of his throat of leather,
'More of More-Hall! O thou rascal!
Would I had seen thee never.
With that thing on thy foot, thou has pierced my gut,
And I'm quite undone for ever.

Murder! Murder!' the dragon cried,
'Alack, alack for grief.
If you had missed that place, you could
Have done me no mischief.'
Then his head he shaked, trembled and quaked,
And down he lay and cried.
First on one knee, then on his back tumbled he,
So groaned, and kicked, and died.

ANONYMOUS

22 The Casualty

Farmers in the fields, housewives behind steamed windows,
Watch the burning aircraft across the blue sky float,
As if a firefly and a spider fought,
Far above the trees, between the washing hung out.
They wait with interest for the evening news.

But already, in a brambled ditch, suddenly-smashed
Stems twitch. In the stubble a pheasant
Is craning every way in astonishment.
The hare that hops up, quizzical, hesitant,
Flattens ears and tears madly away and the wren warns.

Some, who saw fall, smoke beckons. They jostle above,
They peer down a sunbeam as if they expected there
A snake in the gloom of the brambles or a rare flower –
See the grave of dead leaves heave suddenly, hear
It was a man fell out of the air alive,

Hear now his groans and senses groping. They rip
The slum of weeds, leaves, barbed coils; they raise
A body that as the breeze touches it glows,
Branding their hands on his bones. Now that he has
No spine, against heaped sheaves they prop him up,

Arrange his limbs in order, open his eye,
Then stand, helpless as ghosts. In a scene
Melting in the August noon, the burned man
Bulks closer greater flesh and blood than their own,
As suddenly the heart's beat shakes his body and the eye

Widens childishly. Sympathies
Fasten to the blood like flies. Here's no heart's more
Open or large than a fist clenched, and in there
Holding close complacency its most dear
Unscratchable diamond. The tears of their eyes

Too tender to let break, start to the edge
Of such horror close as mourners can,
Greedy to share all that is undergone,
Grimace, gasp, gesture of death. Till they look down
On the handkerchief at which his eye stares up.

TED HUGHES

23 The Ravens Nest

huge   Upon the collar of an hugh old oak
Year after year boys mark a curious nest
Of twigs made up a faggot near in size
And boys to reach it try all sorts of schemes
But not a twig to reach with hand or foot
Sprouts from the pillared trunk and as to try
To swarm the massy bulk tis all in vain
They scarce one effort make to hitch them up
slither   But down they sluther soon as ere they try
So long hath been their dwelling there – old men
When passing bye will laugh and tell the ways
They had when boys to climb that very tree
And as it so would seem that very nest
That ne'er was missing from that self same spot
A single year in all their memorys
And they will say that the two birds are now
The very birds that owned the dwelling then
Some think it strange yet certaintys at loss
And cannot contradict it so they pass
As old birds living the woods patriarchs
Old as the oldest men so famed and known
That even men will thirst into the fame
Of boys at get at schemes that now and then
May captivate a young one from the tree

hooks   With iron claums and bands adventuring up
The mealy trunk or else by waggon ropes
Slung over the hugh grains and so drawn up
By those at bottom one assends secure
With foot rope stirruped – still a perrilous way
So perrilous that one and only one
In memorys of the oldest men was known
To wear his boldness to intentions end
And reach the ravens nest – and thence acchieved
A theme that wonder treasured for supprise
By every cottage hearth the village through
Not yet forgot though other darers come
With daring times that scale the steeples top
And tye their kerchiefs to the weather cock
As trophys that the dangerous deed was done
Yet even now in these adventureous days
No one is bold enough to dare the way
Up the old monstrous oak where every spring
Finds the two ancient birds at their old task
Repairing the hugh nest – where still they live
Through changes winds and storms and are secure
And like a landmark in the chronicles
Of village memorys treasured up yet lives
The hugh old oak that wears the ravens nest

JOHN CLARE

24 Bird Scaring

1   Vlee away, blackie cap,
Don't ye hurt measter's crap,
While I vil my tatie-trap
And lie down and teak a nap.

2   Pigeons and crows
Take care of your toes,
Or I'll pick up my crackers,
And knock you down backwards.
Shoo all away, shoo away, shoo.

TRADITIONAL

25 First Blood

It was. The breech smelling of oil,
The stock of resin – buried snug
In the shoulder. Not too much recoil
At the firing of the first slug

(Jubilantly into the air)
Nor yet too little. Targets pinned
Against a tree: shot down: and there
Abandoned to the sniping wind.

My turn first to carry the gun.
Indian file and camouflaged
With contours of green shade and sun
We ghosted between larch and larch.

A movement between branches – thump
Of a fallen cone. The barrel
Jumps, making branches jump
Higher, dislodging the squirrel

To the next tree. Your turn, my turn.
The silhouette retracts its head.
A hit. 'Let's go back to the lawn.'
'We can't leave it carrying lead

'For the rest of its life. Reload.
Finish him off. Reload again.'
It was now *him*, and when he showed
The sky cracked like a window pane.

He broke away: traversed a full
Half dozen trees: vanished. Had found
A hole? We watched that terrible
Slow spiral to the clubbing ground.

His back was to the tree. His eyes
Were gun barrels. He was dumb,
And we could not see past the size
Of his hands or hear for the drum

In his side. Four shots point-blank
To dull his eyes, a fifth to stop
The shiver in his clotted flank.
A fling of earth. As we stood up

The larches closed their ranks. And when
Earth would not muffle the drumming blood
We, like dishonoured soldiers, ran
The gauntlet of a darkening wood.

JON STALLWORTHY

26 The Combe

The Combe was ever dark, ancient and dark.
Its mouth is stopped with bramble, thorn, and briar ;
And no one scrambles over the sliding chalk
By beech and yew and perishing juniper
Down the half precipices of its sides, with roots
And rabbit holes for steps. The sun of Winter,
The moon of Summer, and all the singing birds
Except the missel-thrush that loves juniper,
Are quite shut out. But far more ancient and dark
The Combe looks since they killed the badger there,
Dug him out and gave him to the hounds,
That most ancient Briton of English beasts.

EDWARD THOMAS

27 Blue Moles

1   They're out of the dark's ragbag, these two
Moles dead in the pebbled rut,
Shapeless as flung gloves, a few feet apart –
Blue suede a dog or fox has chewed.
One, by himself, seemed pitiable enough,
Little victim unearthed by some large creature
From his orbit under the elm root.
The second carcase makes a duel of the affair :
Blind twins bitten by bad nature.

The sky's far dome is sane and clear.
Leaves, undoing their yellow caves
Between the road and the lake water,
Bare no sinister spaces. Already
The moles look neutral as the stones.
Their corkscrew noses, their white hands
Uplifted, stiffen in a family pose.
Difficult to imagine how fury struck –
Dissolved now, smoke of an old war.

2   Nightly the battle-shouts start up
In the ear of the veteran, and again
I enter the soft pelt of the mole.
Light's death to them : they shrivel in it.
They move through their mute rooms while I sleep,
Palming the earth aside, grubbers
After the fat children of root and rock.
By day, only the topsoil heaves.
Down there one is alone.

Outsize hands prepare a path,
They go before : opening the veins,
Delving for the appendages
Of beetles, sweetbreads, shards – to be eaten
Over and over. And still the heaven
Of final surfeit is just as far
From the door as ever. What happens between us
Happens in darkness, vanishes
Easy and often as each breath.

SYLVIA PLATH

28 Ballade to a Fish of the Brooke

Why flyest thou away with fear?
Trust me, there's nought of danger near,
    I have no wicked hooke
All covered with a snaring bait,
Alas, to tempt thee to thy fate,
    And dragge thee from the brooke.

O harmless tenant of the flood,
I do not wish to spill thy blood,
    For Nature unto thee
Perchance hath given a tender wife,
And children dear, to charme thy life,
    As she hath done for me.

Enjoy thy streams, O harmless fish;
And when an angler, for his dish,
    Through gluttony's vile sin,
Attempts, a wretch, to pull thee *out,*
God give thee strength, O gentel trout,
    To pull the raskall *in*!

JOHN WOLCOT

29 The Physician and the Monkey

A lady sent lately for one Doctor *Drug,*
To come in an Instant, and clyster poor Pug –
As the Fair one commanded he came at the Word,
And did the Grand-Office in Tie-Wig and Sword.
    The Affair being ended, so sweet and so nice,
He held out his Hand with, 'You know, Ma'am, my price.'
'Your Price!' says the Lady – 'Why, Sir, he's a Brother,
And Doctors must never take Fees of each other.'

CHRISTOPHER SMART

30 Alley Rats

They were calling certain styles of whiskers by the name of
   'lilacs'.
And another manner of beard assumed in their chatter a verbal
   guise
Of 'mutton chops', 'galways', 'feather dusters'.

Metaphors such as these sprang from their lips while other
   street cries
Sprang from sparrows finding scattered oats among interstices
   of the curb.
Ah-hah these metaphors – and Ah-hah these boys – among the
   police they were known
As the Dirty Dozen and their names took the front pages of
   newspapers
And two of them croaked on the same day at a 'necktie party'
   . . . if we employ the metaphors of their lips.

CARL SANDBURG

31 The Mosquito

When did you start your tricks,
Monsieur?

What do you stand on such high legs for?
Why this length of shredded shank,
You exaltation?

Is it so that you shall lift your centre of gravity upwards
And weigh no more than air as you alight upon me,
Stand upon me weightless, you phantom?

I heard a woman call you the Winged Victory
In sluggish Venice.
You turn your head towards your tail, and smile.

How can you put so much devilry
Into that translucent phantom shred
Of a frail corpus?

Queer, with your thin wings and your streaming legs,
How you sail like a heron, or a dull clot of air,
A nothingness.

Yet what an aura surrounds you;
Your evil little aura, prowling, and casting a numbness on
    my mind.

That is your trick, your bit of filthy magic:
Invisibility, and the anaesthetic power
To deaden my attention in your direction.

But I know your game now, streaky sorcerer.
Queer, how you stalk and prowl the air
In circles and evasions, enveloping me,
Ghoul on wings
Winged Victory.

Settle, and stand on long thin shanks
Eyeing me sideways, and cunningly conscious that I am aware,
You speck.

I hate the way you lurch off sideways into air
Having read my thoughts against you.

Come then, let us play at unawares,
And see who wins in this sly game of bluff.
Man or mosquito.

You don't know that I exist, and I don't know that you exist.
Now then!

It is your trump,
It is your hateful little trump,
You pointed fiend,
Which shakes my sudden blood to hatred of you:
It is your small, high, hateful bugle in my ear.

Why do you do it?
Surely it is bad policy.

They say you can't help it.

If that is so, then I believe a little in Providence protecting the
    innocent.
But it sounds so amazingly like a slogan,
A yell of triumph as you snatch my scalp.

Blood, red blood
Super-magical
Forbidden liquor.

I behold you stand
For a second enspasmed in oblivion,
Obscenely ecstasied
Sucking live blood,
My blood.

Such silence, such suspended transport,
Such gorging,
Such obscenity of trespass.

You stagger
As well as you may.
Only your accursed hairy frailty,
Your own imponderable weightlessness
Saves you, wafts you away on the very draught my anger makes
    in its snatching.

Away with a paean of derision,
You winged blood-drop.

Can I not overtake you?
Are you one too many for me,
Winged Victory?
Am I not mosquito enough to out-mosquito you?

Queer what a big stain my sucked blood makes
Beside the infinitesimal faint smear of you!
Queer, what a dim dark smudge you have disappeared into!

D. H. LAWRENCE

32 The Fish

I caught a tremendous fish
and held him beside the boat
half out of water, with my hook
fast in a corner of his mouth.
He didn't fight.
He hadn't fought at all.
He hung a grunting weight,
battered and venerable
and homely. Here and there
his brown skin hung in strips
like ancient wall-paper,
and its pattern of darker brown
was like wall-paper :
shapes like full-blown roses
stained and lost through age.
He was speckled with barnacles,
fine rosettes of lime,
and infested
with tiny white sea-lice,
and underneath two or three
rags of green weed hung down.
While his gills were breathing in
the terrible oxygen
– the frightening gills
fresh and crisp with blood,
that can cut so badly –
I thought of the coarse white flesh
packed in like feathers,
the big bones and the little bones,
the dramatic reds and blacks
of his shiny entrails,
and the pink swim-bladder
like a big peony.
I looked into his eyes
which were far larger than mine
but shallower, and yellowed,
the irises backed and packed
with tarnished tinfoil
seen through the lenses

mica of old scratched isinglass.
They shifted a little, but not
to return my stare.
– It was more like the tipping
of an object toward the light.
I admired his sullen face,
the mechanism of his jaw,
and then I saw
that from his lower lip
– if you could call it a lip –
grim, wet, and weapon-like,
hung five old pieces of fish-line,
or four and a wire leader
with the swivel still attached,
with all their five big hooks
grown firmly in his mouth.
A green line, frayed at the end
where he broke it, two heavier lines,
and a fine black thread
still crimped from the strain and snap
when it broke and he got away.
Like medals with their ribbons
frayed and wavering,
a five-haired beard of wisdom
trailing from his aching jaw.
I stared and stared
and victory filled up
the little rented boat,
from the pool of bilge
where oil had spread a rainbow
around the rusted engine
to the bailer rusted orange,
the sun-cracked thwarts,
the oarlocks on their strings,
the gunnels – until everything
was rainbow, rainbow, rainbow !
And I let the fish go.

ELIZABETH BISHOP

33 The Ox-Tamer

In a far-away northern country in the placid pastoral region,
Lives my farmer-friend, the theme of my recitative, a famous
    tamer of oxen,
There they bring him the three-year-olds and the four-year-olds
    to break them,
He will take the wildest steer in the world and break him and
    tame him,
He will go fearless without any whip where the young bullock
    chafes up and down the yard,
The bullock's head tosses restless high in the air with raging eyes,
Yet see you! how soon his rage subsides – how soon this tamer
    tames him;
See you! on the farms hereabouts a hundred oxen young and old,
    and he is the man who has tamed them,
They all know him, all are affectionate to him;
See you! some are such beautiful animals, so lofty looking;
Some are buff-colour'd, some mottled, one has a white line
    running along his back, some are brindled.
Some have wide flaring horns (a good sign) – see you! the bright
    hides,
See, the two with stars on their foreheads – see, the round bodies
    and broad backs,
How straight and square they stand on their legs – what fine
    sagacious eyes!
How they watch their tamer – they wish him near them – how
    they turn to look after him!
What yearning expression! how uneasy they are when he moves
    away from them;
Now I marvel what it can be he appears to them (books,
    politics, poems, depart–all else departs),
I confess I envy only his fascination – my silent, illiterate friend,
Whom a hundred oxen love there in his life on farms,
In the northern country far, in the placid pastoral region.

WALT WHITMAN

34 The Marten

The martin cat long shaged of courage good
Of weazle shape a dweller in the wood
With badger hair long shagged and darting eyes
And lower then the common cat in size
Small head and running on the stoop
Snuffing the ground and hind parts shouldered up
He keeps one track and hides in lonely shade
Where print of human foot is scarcely made
Save when the woods are cut the beaten track
The woodman's dog will snuff cock-tailed and black
Red legged and spotted over either eye
Snuffs barks and scrats the lice and passes bye
The great brown horned owl looks down below
And sees the shaggy martin come and go

The martin hurrys through the woodland gaps
And poachers shoot and make his skin for caps
When any woodman come and pass the place
He looks at dogs and scarcely mends his pace
And gipseys often and birdnesting boys
Look in the hole and hear a hissing noise
They climb the tree such noise they never heard
And think the great owl is a foreign bird
When the grey owl her young ones cloathed in down
Seizes the boldest boy and drives him down
They try agen and pelt to start the fray
The grey owl comes and drives them all away
And leaves the martin twisting round his den
Left free from boys and dogs and noise and men

JOHN CLARE

35 How a Good Greyhound is Shaped

A head like a snake, a neck like a drake,
A back like a beam, a belly like a bream,
A foot like a cat, a tail like a rat.

TRADITIONAL

36 Water Picture

In the pond in the park
all things are doubled :
Long buildings hang and
wriggle gently. Chimneys
are bent legs bouncing
on clouds below. A flag
wags like a fishhook
down there in the sky.

The arched stone bridge
is an eye, with underlid
in the water. In its lens
dip crinkled heads with hats
that don't fall off. Dogs go by,
barking on their backs.
A baby, taken to feed the
ducks, dangles upside-down,
a pink balloon for a buoy.

Treetops deploy a haze of
cherry bloom for roots,
where birds coast belly-up
in the glass bowl of a hill ;
from its bottom a bunch
of peanut-munching children
is suspended by their
sneakers, waveringly.

A swan, with twin necks
forming the figure three,
steers between two dimpled
towers doubled. Fondly,
hissing, she kisses herself,
and all the scene is troubled :
water-windows splinter,
tree-limbs tangle, the bridge
folds like a fan.

MAY SWENSON

37 Death of a Naturalist

All year the flax-dam festered in the heart
Of the townland; green and heavy headed
Flax had rotted there, weighted down by huge sods.
Daily it sweltered in the punishing sun.
Bubbles gargled delicately, bluebottles
Wove a strong gauze of sound around the smell.
There were dragon-flies, spotted butterflies,
But best of all was the warm thick slobber
Of frogspawn that grew like clotted water
In the shade of the banks. Here, every spring
I would fill jampotfuls of the jellied
Specks to range on window-sills at home,
On shelves at school, and wait and watch until
The fattening dots burst into nimble-
Swimming tadpoles. Miss Walls would tell us how
The daddy frog was called a bullfrog
And how he croaked and how the mammy frog
Laid hundreds of little eggs and this was
Frogspawn. You could tell the weather by frogs too
For they were yellow in the sun and brown
In rain.
       Then one hot day when fields were rank
With cowdung in the grass the angry frogs
Invaded the flax-dam; I ducked through hedges
To a coarse croaking that I had not heard
Before. The air was thick with a bass chorus.
Right down the dam gross-bellied frogs were cocked
On sods; their loose necks pulsed like sails. Some hopped:
The slap and plop were obscene threats. Some sat
Poised like mud grenades, their blunt heads farting.
I sickened, turned, and ran. The great slime kings
Were gathered there for vengeance and I knew
That if I dipped my hand the spawn would clutch it.

SEAMUS HEANEY

38 Mushrooms

Overnight, very
Whitely, discreetly,
Very quietly

Our toes, our noses
Take hold on the loam,
Acquire the air.

Nobody sees us,
Stops us, betrays us ;
The small grains make room.

Soft fists insist on
Heaving the needles,
The leafy bedding,

Even the paving.
Our hammers, our rams,
Earless and eyeless,

Perfectly voiceless,
Widen the crannies,
Shoulder through holes. We

Diet on water,
On crumbs of shadow,
Bland-mannered, asking

Little or nothing.
So many of us !
So many of us !

We are shelves, we are
Tables, we are meek,
We are edible,

Nudgers and shovers
In spite of ourselves.
Our kind multiplies :

We shall by morning
Inherit the earth.
Our foot's in the door.

SYLVIA PLATH

39 The Spider

Just as my fingers close about the pen,
a spider, smaller than a grain of sand,
proceeds from nail to knuckle; pauses; then
starts the vast exploration of my hand.
Hastily tramping through warm wastes it goes
careless of curving hairs and rutted skin,
earthquakes of muscle, great volcanic throes
of blood and flesh beneath, scorning the din
of monstrous nostril-gales that blast its way
from wrist to elbow, where the white ascent
of one world-column starts. 'Now fail!' I say.
It does not even ponder what I meant,
    but moves up through an atmosphere grown colder
    towards the uncharted mountain of my shoulder.

KENNETH MACKENZIE

40 Death of a Whale

When the mouse died, there was a sort of pity;
The tiny, delicate creature made for grief.
Yesterday, instead, the dead whale on the reef
Drew an excited multitude to the jetty.
How must a whale die to wring a tear?
Lugubrious death of a whale; the big
Feast for the gulls and sharks; the tug
Of the tide simulating life still there,
Until the air, polluted, swings this way
Like a door ajar from a slaughterhouse.
Pooh! pooh! spare us, give us the death of a mouse
By its tiny hole; not this in our lovely bay.
- Sorry, we are, too, when a child dies:
But at the immolation of a race, who cries?

JOHN BLIGHT

41 Written on the Adder's Belly

If I could hear as well as see,
No man or beast should pass by me.

TRADITIONAL

42 A Cure for Adder-Bite

hazel twig

'Underneath this hazelin mote,
There's a bragotty worm with a speckled throat,
Nine double is he;
Now from eight double to seven double,
And from seven double to six double . . .'
and so on to –
'And from one double to no double,
No double hath he.'

TRADITIONAL

43 Medallion

By the gate with star and moon
Worked into the peeled orange wood
The bronze snake lay in the sun

Inert as a shoelace; dead
But pliable still, his jaw
Unhinged and his grin crooked,

Tongue a rose-coloured arrow.
Over my hand I hung him.
His little vermilion eye

Ignited with a glassed flame
As I turned him in the light;
When I split a rock one time

The garnet bits burned like that.
Dust dulled his back to ochre
The way sun ruins a trout.

Yet his belly kept its fire
Going under the chainmail,
The old jewels smouldering there

In each opaque belly-scale :
Sunset looked at through milk glass.
And I saw white maggots coil

Thin as pins in the dark bruise
Where his innards bulged as if
He were digesting a mouse.

Knifelike, he was chaste enough,
Pure death's-metal. The yardman's
Flung brick perfected his laugh.

SYLVIA PLATH

44 To the Snake

Green Snake, when I hung you round my neck
and stroked your cold, pulsing throat
        as you hissed to me, glinting
arrowy gold scales, and I felt
        the weight of you on my shoulders,
and the whispering silver of your dryness
        sounded close at my ears —

Green Snake — I swore to my companions that certainly
        you were harmless ! But truly
I had no certainty, and no hope, only desiring
        to hold you, for that joy,
                        which left
a long wake of pleasure, as the leaves moved
and you faded into the pattern
of grass and shadows, and I returned
smiling and haunted, to a dark morning.

DENISE LEVERTOV

45 Original Sin

The man-brained and man-handed ground-ape, physically
The most repulsive of all hot-blooded animals
Up to that time of the world: they had dug a pitfall
And caught a mammoth, but how could their sticks and stones
Reach the life in that hide? They danced around the pit,
     shrieking
With ape excitement, flinging sharp flints in vain, and the
     stench of their bodies
Stained the white air of dawn; but presently one of them
Remembered the yellow dancer, wood-eating fire
That guards the cave-mouth: he ran and fetched him, and
     others
Gathered sticks at the wood's edge; they made a blaze
And pushed it into the pit, and they fed it high, around the
     mired sides
Of their huge prey. They watched the long hairy trunk
Waver over the stifle-trumpeting pain,
And they were happy.

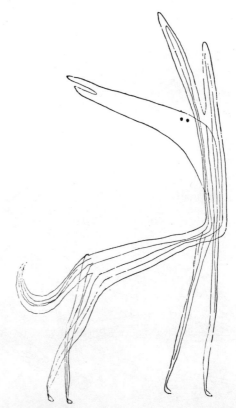

Meanwhile the intense color and
nobility of sunrise.
Rose and gold and amber, flowed up the sky. Wet rocks were
shining, a little wind
Stirred the leaves of the forest and the marsh flag-flowers;
the soft valley between the low hills
Became as beautiful as the sky; while in its midst, hour
after hour, the happy hunters
Roasted their living meat slowly to death.
These are the
people.
This is the human dawn. As for me, I would rather
Be a worm in a wild apple than a son of man.
But we are what we are, and we might remember
Not to hate any person, for all are vicious;
And not be astonished at any evil, all are deserved;
And not fear death; it is the only way to be cleansed.

ROBINSON JEFFERS

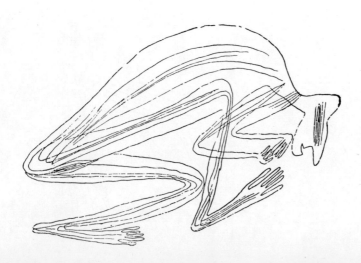

46 The Hunting Man

Riding along the winter's gentle heat
Let every huntsman hear the fox's curse,
Let every soldier see a flowered hearse;
    The biter bitten, the bitter sweet.

Riding along through winter's leaden rain
Let every huntsman fear the hidden wire,
Let every soldier dread the ambushed fire;
    The victor vanquished, the slayer slain.

RONALD BOTTRALL

47 Ground-Hog

Whet up yer knife and whistle up yer dogs, (*twice*)
Away to the hills to catch ground-hogs.
            Ground-Hog!

They picked up their guns and went to the braish, (*twice*)
By damn, Bill, here's a hog-sign fraish.
            Ground-Hog!

Hunker down, Sam, and in there peep, (*twice*)
For I think I see him sound asleep.
            Ground-Hog!

Run here, Johnny, with a great long pole, (*twice*)
And roust this ground-hog outer his hole.
            Ground-Hog!

Work, boys, work, as hard as you can tear, (*twice*)
This meat'll do to eat and the hide'll do to wear.
            Ground-Hog!

I heard him give a whistle and a wail, (*twice*)
And I wound my stick around his tail.
            Ground-Hog!

Scrape him down to his head and feet, (*twice*)
Lordy, boys, there's a fine pile o' meat.
            Ground-Hog!

They put him in the pot and all began to smile, (*twice*)
They et that ground hog 'fore he struck a bile.
   Ground-Hog!

The children screamed and the children cried, (*twice*)
They love ground-hog cooked and fried.
   Ground-Hog!

Up stepped Sal with a snigger and a grin, (*twice*)
Ground-hog grease all over her chin.
   Ground-Hog!

Run here, Mama, run here, quick, (*twice*)
I think that ground-hog's makin' me sick.
   Ground-Hog!

Run here, Mama, make Bill quit, (*twice*)
He's et all the ground-hog an' I ain't had a bit.
   Ground-Hog!

Ol' Aunt Sal come a-skippin' through the hall, (*twice*)
Got enough ground-hog to feed um all.
   GROUND-HOG!

TRADITIONAL AMERICAN

48 The Pardon

My dog lay dead five days without a grave
In the thick of summer, hid in a clump of pine
And a jungle of grass and honeysuckle-vine.
I who had loved him while he kept alive

Went only close enough to where he was
To sniff the heavy honeysuckle-smell
Twined with another odor heavier still
And hear the flies' intolerable buzz.

Well, I was ten and very much afraid.
In my kind world the dead were out of range
And I could not forgive the sad or strange
In beast or man. My father took the spade

And buried him. Last night I saw the grass
Slowly divide (it was the same scene
But now it glowed a fierce and mortal green)
And saw the dog emerging. I confess

I felt afraid again, but still he came
In the carnal sun, clothed in a hymn of flies,
And death was breeding in his lively eyes.
I started in to cry and call his name,

Asking forgiveness of his tongueless head.
. . . I dreamt the past was never past redeeming :
But whether this was false or honest dreaming
I beg death's pardon now. And mourn the dead.

RICHARD WILBUR

49 Old Blue

I had an ol' dog, boys, and I called him Blue,
Listen lemme tell you what Blue could do.
>   Come on, Blue, you good dog, you.
>   Yes, come on, Blue, you good dog, you.

I took my axe, boys, and I blowed my horn,
Goin' a-huntin' just as shore's you're born.
>   Come on, Blue, you good dog, you.
>   Yes, come on, Blue, you good dog, you.

Old Blue treed and I went to see,
Had him a possum up a white-oak tree.
>   Come on, Blue, you good dog, you.
>   Yes, come on, Blue, you good dog, you.

He growled at me, I looked at him,
I shook him out, Blue took him in.
>   Come on, Blue, you good dog, you.
>   Yes, come on, Blue, you good dog, you.

Baked that possum good and brown,
Laid them sweet 'taters round and round.
>   Says, come on, Blue, you can have some, too.
>   Yes, come on, Blue, you can have some, too.

The doctor's come, an' he come on the run,
He says, 'Old Blue, your huntin' is done.'
   Come on, Blue, you good dog, you.
   Yes, come on, Blue, you good dog, you.

Old Blue died, an' he died so hard,
He dug up the ground all over the yard.
   Go on, Blue, you good dog, you.
   Yes, go on, Blue, you good dog, you.

When I get to heaven, I know what I'll do,
Grab my horn and blow for old Blue.
   Sayin', 'Come here, Blue, I've got here, too.'
   Sayin', 'Come here, Blue, I've got here, too.'

And when I hear my old Blue dog bark,
I'll know he's treed a 'possum in Noah's Ark.
   Sayin', 'Come here, Blue, I've got here, too.'
   Sayin', 'Come here, Blue, I've got here, too.'

TRADITIONAL AMERICAN

50 Bags of Meat

'Here's a fine bag of meat,'
Says the master-auctioneer,
As the timid, quivering steer,
Starting a couple of feet
At the prod of a drover's stick,
And trotting lightly and quick,
A ticket stuck on his rump,
Enters with a bewildered jump.

'Where he's lived lately, friends,
I'd live till lifetime ends:
They've a whole life everyday
Down there in the Vale, have they!
He'd be worth the money to kill
And give away Christmas for good-will.'

'Now here's a heifer – worth more
Than bid, were she bone-poor;
Yet she's round as a barrel of beer;'
'She's a plum,' said the second auctioneer.

'Now this young bull – for thirty pound?
Worth that to manure your ground!'
'Or to stand,' chimed the second one,
'And have his picter done!'

The beast was rapped on the horns and snout
To make him turn about.
'Well,' cried a buyer, 'another crown –
Since I've dragged here from Taunton Town!'

'That calf, she sucked three cows,
drink   Which is not matched for bouse
In the nurseries of high life
By the first-born of a nobleman's wife!'
The stick falls, meaning, 'A true tale's told,'
On the buttock of the creature sold,
And the buyer leans over and snips
His mark on one of the animal's hips.

Each beast, when driven in,
Looks round at the ring of bidders there
With a much-amazed reproachful stare,
As at unnatural kin,
For bringing him to a sinister scene
So strange, unhomelike, hungry, mean;
His fate the while suspended between
A butcher, to kill out of hand,
And a farmer, to keep on the land;
One can fancy a tear runs down his face
When the butcher wins, and he's driven from the place.

THOMAS HARDY

51 Travelling Through the Dark

Travelling through the dark I found a deer
dead on the edge of the Wilson River road.
It is usually best to roll them into the canyon:
that road is narrow; to swerve might make more dead.

By glow of the tail-light I stumbled back of the car
and stood by the heap, a doe, a recent killing;
she had stiffened already, almost cold.
I dragged her off; she was large in the belly.

My fingers touching her side brought me the reason –
her side was warm; her fawn lay there waiting,
alive, still, never to be born.
Beside that mountain road I hesitated.

The car aimed ahead its lowered parking lights;
under the hood purred the steady engine.
I stood in the glare of the warm exhaust turning red;
around our group I could hear the wilderness listen.

I thought hard for us all – my only swerving –
then pushed her over the edge into the river.

WILLIAM STAFFORD

52 The Fox

When I saw the fox, it was kneeling
in snow: there was nothing to confess
that, tipped on its broken forepaws
the thing was dead – save for its stillness.

A drift, confronting me, leaned down
across the hill-top field. The wind
had scarped it into a pennine wholly of snow, and
where did the hill go now?

There was no way round:
I drew booted legs
back out of it, took to my tracks again,
but already a million blown snow-motes were
   flowing and filling them in.

Domed at the summit, then tapering,
the drift still mocked
my mind as if the whole
fox-infested hill were the skull of a fox.

Scallops and dips
of pure pile rippled and shone, but what
should I do with such beauty
eyed by that?

It was like clambering between its white temples
as the crosswind tore
at one's knees, and each
missed step was a plunge at the hill's blinding interior.

CHARLES TOMLINSON

53 Self-Pity

I never saw a wild thing
sorry for itself.
A small bird will drop frozen dead from a bough
without ever having felt sorry for itself.

D. H. LAWRENCE

54 The Darlaston Dog Fight

Down Sewerage Street where the smell ain't so sweet
Rough Moey flopped down on his flat-bottomed feet,
And under his arm The Pride of 'Em All,
The bitch as could bite a bolt hole through a wall.

And back of the Bull Stake by Darlaston Green,
Ben Bates brought his bitch, the Willenhall Queen;
The Queen had a mouth like a shark with the yaws,
And God help the dog as got stuck in her jaws.

At scratch on the sewer a hundred were stood,
They'd all backed their fancy and thirsted for blood.
They backed with the bookie each bitch at odds on,
No matter who lost, he knew he had won.

grooms   The lickers licked hard and they licked very well,
They dain't miss a hair on them dogs – you can tell;
A tot or two more and instead of a dog
They'd have licked all the spikes on a spavined hedgehog.

Old Reuben was made referee of the match,
The Pride and The Queen was brought up to scratch,
The bell for the start the timekeeper smote,
And both of them dogs went for each other's throat.

The Queen missed The Pride and Ben Bates shed a tear,
The Pride missed The Queen with a snap you could hear.
Five minutes went by with no sign of a bite,
It was more like a dance than a fighting dog fight.

Rough cussed for a coward The Pride of 'Em All,
The Pride seemed too drunk to be bothered at all.
And as for The Queen, Ben Bates hung his head,
And cried to the crowd to say prayers for the dead.

Then into the pit jumped Rough Mo' with a roar,
He fell on his face and lay flat on the floor,
And then he found out why them dogs wouldn't bite:
Sewer gas in the pit: they was too drugged to fight.

Rough Mo' had a lungful and didn't feel too well,
He bit at them dogs – they bit back, you can tell,
The Queen had a bite that took half of his ear,
The Pride had a mouthful of ham off his rear.

No matter how Rough urged them dogs on to fight,
They both was too drugged and too beggared to bite.
He kicked at The Queen which collapsed on the floor,
And Ben kicked at Rough where his backside was sore.

67

Them dogs at each other could not point a paw,
And Reuben declared that the match was a draw.
cried   The bookmaker blarted – he had to pay back
The money he thought was his own in the sack.

That fight was the last by Ben Bates and his Queen,
Broken-hearted they died in the pub by the Green ;
Rough Moey has never been able to sit
The same as afore he got bit in the pit.

TOM LANGLEY

55   Skunks

The corruptions of war and peace, the public and whole-
    sale crimes that make war, the greed and lies of the
    peace
And victor's vengeance : how at a distance
They soften into romance – blue mountains and blos-
    somed marshes in the long landscape of history –
    Caligula
Becomes an amusing clown, and Genghiz
A mere genius, a great author of tragedies. Our own
    time's chiefs of massacre – Stalin died yesterday –
Watch how soon blood will bleach, and gross horror
Becomes words in a book.
                     We have little animals here,
    slow-stepping cousins of stoat and weasel,
Striped skunks, that can spit from under their tails
An odor so vile and stifling that neither wolf nor wild-
    cat dares to come near them ; they walk in confi-
    dence,
Solely armed with this loathsome poison-gas.
But smelled far off – have you noticed ? – it is surpris-
    ingly pleasant.
              It is like the breath of ferns and wet
    earth
Deep in a wooded glen in the evening,
Cool water glides quietly over the moss-grown stones,
    quick trout dimple the pool. – Distance makes clean.

ROBINSON JEFFERS

56 Fighting South of the Castle

They fought south of the Castle,
They died north of the wall.
They died in the moors and were not buried.
Their flesh was the food of crows.
'Tell the crows we are not afraid;
We have died in the moors and cannot be buried.
Crows, how can our bodies escape you?'
The waters flowed deep
And the rushes in the pool were dark.
The riders fought and were slain:
Their horses wander neighing.
By the bridge there was a house.
Was it south, was it north?
The harvest was never gathered.
How can we give you your offerings?
You served your Prince faithfully,
Though all in vain.
I think of you, faithful soldiers;
Your service shall not be forgotten.
For in the morning you went out to battle
And at night you did not return.

ANONYMOUS Translated from the Chinese by Arthur Waley

57 The Vote

The helmet now an hive for bees becomes,
And hilts of swords may serve for spiders' looms;
    Sharp pikes may make
    Teeth for a rake;
And the keen blade, th'arch enemy of life,
Shall be degraded to a pruning knife.
    The rustic spade
    Which first was made
For honest agriculture, shall retake
Its primitive employment, and forsake
ramparts   The rampires steep
    And trenches deep.

Tame conies in our brazen guns shall breed,
Or gentle doves their young ones there shall feed.
    In musket barrels
    Mice shall raise quarrels
For their quarters. The ventriloquious drum,
Like lawyers in vacations, shall be dumb.
    Now all recruits,
    But those of fruits,
Shall be forgot; and th'unarmed soldier

erewhile Shall only boast of what he did whilere,
    In chimneys' ends
    Among his friends.

If good effects shall happy signs ensue,
I shall rejoice, and my prediction's true.

RALPH KNEVET

58   Triumphal March

Stone, bronze, stone, steel, stone, oakleaves, horses' heels
Over the paving.
And the flags. And the trumpets. And so many eagles.
How many? Count them. And such a press of people.
We hardly knew ourselves that day, or knew the City.
This is the way to the temple, and we so many crowding the
    way.
So many waiting, how many waiting? what did it matter, on
    such a day?
Are they coming? No, not yet. You can see some eagles. And
    hear the trumpets.
Here they come. Is he coming?
The natural wakeful life of our Ego is a perceiving.
We can wait with our stools and our sausages.
What comes first? Can you see? Tell us. It is

    5,800,000 rifles and carbines,
      102,000 machine guns,
      28,000 trench mortars,
      53,000 field and heavy guns,
I cannot tell how many projectiles, mines and fuses,

```
                  13,000 aeroplanes,
                  24,000 aeroplane engines,
                  50,000 ammunition waggons,
        now       55,000 army waggons,
                  11,000 field kitchens,
                   1,150 field bakeries.
```

What a time that took. Will it be he now? No,
Those are the golf club Captains, these the Scouts,
And now the *société gymnastique de Poissy*
And now come the Mayor and the Liverymen. Look
There he is now, look:
There is no interrogation in those eyes
Or in the hands, quiet over the horse's neck,
And the eyes watchful, waiting, perceiving, indifferent.
O hidden under the dove's wing, hidden in the turtle's breast,
Under the palmtree at noon, under the running water
At the still point of the turning world. O hidden.

Now they go up to the temple. Then the sacrifice.
Now come the virgins bearing urns, urns containing
Dust
Dust
Dust of dust, and now
Stone, bronze, stone, steel, stone, oakleaves, horses' heels
Over the paving.

That is all we could see. But how many eagles! and how many
    trumpets!
(And Easter Day, we didn't get to the country,
So we took young Cyril to church. And they rang a bell
And he said right out loud, *crumpets*.)
                              Don't throw away that sausage,
It'll come in handy. He's artful. Please, will you
Give us a light?
Light
Light
Et les soldats faisaient la haie? ILS LA FAISAIENT.

T. S. ELIOT

59 The Drum

I hate that drum's discordant sound,
Parading round, and round, and round:
To thoughtless youth it pleasure yields,
And lures from cities and from fields,
To sell their liberty for charms
Of tawdry lace, and glittering arms;
And when Ambition's voice commands,
To march, and fight, and fall, in foreign lands.

I hate that drum's discordant sound,
Parading round, and round, and round:
To me it talks of ravaged plains,
And burning towns, and ruined swains,
And mangled limbs, and dying groans,
And widows' tears, and orphans' moans;
And all that Misery's hand bestows,
To fill the catalogue of human woes.

JOHN SCOTT

60 Beach Burial

Softly and humbly to the Gulf of Arabs
The convoys of dead sailors come;
At night they sway and wander in the waters far under,
But morning rolls them in the foam.

Between the sob and clubbing of the gunfire
Someone, it seems, has time for this,
To pluck them from the shallows and bury them in burrows
And tread the sand upon their nakedness;

And each cross, the driven stake of tidewood,
Bears the last signature of men,
Written with such perplexity, with such bewildered pity,
The words choke as they begin —

'*Unknown seaman*' – the ghostly pencil
Wavers and fades, the purple drips;
The breath of the wet season has washed their inscriptions
As blue as drowned men's lips,

Dead seamen, gone in search of the same landfall,
Whether as enemies they fought,
Or fought with us, or neither; the sand joins them together,
Enlisted on the other front.

El Alamein

KENNETH SLESSOR

61 Hearing that his Friend was Coming Back from the War

In old days those who went to fight
In three years had one year's leave.
But in *this* war the soldiers are never changed;
They must go on fighting till they die on the battlefield.
I thought of you, so weak and indolent,
Hopelessly trying to learn to march and drill.
That a young man should ever come home again
Seemed about as likely as that the sky should fall.
Since I got the news that you were coming back,
Twice I have mounted to the high wall of your home.
I found your brother mending your horse's stall;
I found your mother sewing your new clothes.
I am half afraid; perhaps it is not true;
Yet I never weary of watching for you on the road
Each day I go out at the City Gate
With a flask of wine, lest you should come thirsty.
Oh that I could shrink the surface of the World,
So that suddenly I might find you standing at my side!

WANG-CHIEN Translated from the Chinese by Arthur Waley

74

62 A Protest in the Sixth Year of Ch'ien Fu
(A.D. 879)

The hills and rivers of the lowland country
    You have made your battle-ground.
How do you suppose the people who live there
    Will procure 'firewood and hay'?
Do not let me hear you talking together
    About titles and promotions;
For a single general's reputation
    Is made out of ten thousand corpses.

TS'AO SUNG Translated from the Chinese by Arthur Waley

63 The Battle

Helmet and rifle, pack and overcoat
Marched through a forest. Somewhere up ahead
Guns thudded. Like the circle of a throat
The night on every side was turning red.

They halted and they dug. They sank like moles
Into the clammy earth between the trees.
And soon the sentries, standing in their holes,
Felt the first snow. Their feet began to freeze.

At dawn the first shell landed with a crack.
Then shells and bullets swept the icy woods.
This lasted many days. The snow was black.
The corpses stiffened in their scarlet hoods.

Most clearly of that battle I remember
The tiredness in eyes, how hands looked thin
Around a cigarette, and the bright ember
Would pulse with all the life there was within.

LOUIS SIMPSON

64 First Snow in Alsace

The snow came down last night like moths
Burned on the moon ; it fell till dawn,
Covered the town with simple cloths.

Absolute snow lies rumpled on
What shellbursts scattered and deranged,
Entangled railings, crevassed lawn.

As if it did not know they'd changed,
Snow smoothly clasps the roofs of homes
Fear-gutted, trustless and estranged.

The ration stacks are milky domes ;
Across the ammunition pile
The snow has climbed in sparkling combs.

You think : beyond the town a mile
Or two, this snowfall fills the eyes
Of soldiers dead a little while.

Persons and persons in disguise,
Walking the new air white and fine,
Trade glances quick with shared surprise.

At children's windows, heaped, benign,
As always, winter shines the most,
And frost makes marvellous designs.

The night guard coming from his post,
Ten first-snows back in thought, walks slow
And warms him with a boyish boast :

He was the first to see the snow.

RICHARD WILBUR

65 The Last Man

'Twas in the year two thousand and one,
A pleasant morning of May,
I sat on the gallows-tree all alone,
A-chanting a merry lay, –
plague   To think how the pest had spared my life,
To sing with the larks that day!

When up the heath came a jolly knave,
Like a scarecrow, all in rags:
rags   It made me crow to see his old duds
All abroad in the wind, like flags:
So up he came to the timbers' foot
And pitch'd down his greasy bags. –

Good Lord! how blythe the old beggar was!
At pulling out his scraps, –
bits of food   The very sight of his broken orts
Made a work in his wrinkled chaps:
'Come down,' says he, 'you Newgate-bird,
And have a taste of my snaps!' –

Then down the rope, like a tar from the mast,
I slided, and by him stood;
But I wish'd myself on the gallows again
When I smelt that beggar's food, –
A foul beef-bone and a mouldy crust; –
'Oh!' quoth he, 'the heavens are good!'

Then after this grace he cast him down:
Says I, 'You'll get sweeter air
A pace or two off, on the windward side,' –
For the felons' bones lay there –
But he only laugh'd at the empty skulls,
And offer'd them part of his fare.

'I never harm'd *them*, and they won't harm me;
Let the proud and the rich be cravens!'
I did not like that strange beggar man,
He look'd so up at the heavens.
Anon he shook out his empty old poke;
'There's the crumbs,' saith he, 'for the ravens!'

It made me angry to see his face,
It had such a jesting look;
But while I made up my mind to speak,
A small case-bottle he took:
Quoth he, 'Though I gather the green water-cress,
My drink is not of the brook!'

Full manners-like he tender'd the dram;
Oh, it came of a dainty cask!
But, whenever it came to his turn to pull,
'Your leave, good Sir, I must ask;
But I always wipe the brim with my sleeve,
When a hangman sups at my flask!'

And then he laugh'd so loudly and long,
The churl was quite out of breath;
I thought the very Old One was come
To mock me before my death,
And wish'd I had buried the dead men's bones
That were lying about the heath!

But the beggar gave me a jolly clap –
'Come, let us pledge each other,
For all the wide world is dead beside,
And we are brother and brother –
I've a yearning for thee in my heart,
As if we had come of one mother.

'I've a yearning for thee in my heart
That almost makes me weep,
For as I pass'd from town to town
The folks were all stone-asleep, –
But when I saw thee sitting aloft,
It made me both laugh and leap!'

Now a curse (I thought) be on his love,
And a curse upon his mirth, –
if An it were not for that beggar man
I'd be the King of the earth, –
But I promised myself, an hour should come
To make him rue his birth! –

So down we sat and bous'd again
Till the sun was in mid-sky,
When, just as the gentle west-wind came,
We hearken'd a dismal cry;
'Up, up, on the tree,' quoth the beggar man,
'Till these horrible dogs go by!'

And lo! from the forest's far-off skirts,
They came all yelling for gore,
A hundred hounds pursuing at once,
And a panting hart before,
Till he sunk adown at the gallows' foot
And there his haunches they tore!

His haunches they tore, without a horn
To tell when the chase was done;
And there was not a single scarlet coat
To flaunt it in the sun! –
I turn'd, and look'd at the beggar man,
And his tears dropt one by one!

And with curses sore he chid at the hounds,
Till the last dropt out of sight,
Anon, saith he, 'Let's down again,
And ramble for our delight,
For the world's all free, and we may choose
A right cozie barn for tonight!'

With that, he set up his staff on end,
And it fell with the point due West;
So we far'd that way to a city great,
Where the folks had died of the pest –
It was fine to enter in house and hall,
Wherever it liked me best; –

For the porters all were stiff and cold,
And could not lift their heads;
And when we came where their masters lay,
The rats leapt out of the beds: –
The grandest palaces in the land
Were as free as workhouse sheds.

But the beggar man made a mumping face,
And knock'd at every gate:
It made me curse to hear how he whin'd,
So our fellowship turn'd to hate,
And I bade him walk the world by himself,
For I scorn'd so humble a mate!

So *he* turn'd right and *I* turn'd left,
As if we had never met;
And I chose a fair stone house for myself,
For the city was all to let;
And for three brave holidays drank my fill
Of the choicest that I could get.

And because my jerkin was coarse and worn,
I got me a properer vest;
It was purple velvet, stitch'd o'er with gold,
And a shining star at the breast, –
'Twas enough to fetch old Joan from her grave
To see me so purely drest! –

But Joan was dead and under the mould,
And every buxom lass;
In vain I watch'd, at the window pane,
For a Christian soul to pass; –
But sheep and kine wander'd up the street,
And browz'd on the new-come grass. –

When lo! I spied the old beggar man,
And lustily he did sing! –
His rags were lapp'd in a scarlet cloak,
And a crown he had like a King;
So he stept right up before my gate
And danced me a saucy fling!

Heaven mend us all! – but, within my mind,
I had kill'd him then and there;
To see him lording so braggart-like
That was born to his beggar's fare,
And how he had stolen the royal crown
His betters were meant to wear.

But God forbid that a thief should die
Without his share of the laws!
So I nimbly whipt my tackle out,
And soon tied up his claws, –
I was judge myself, and jury, and all,
And solemnly tried the cause.

But the beggar man would not plead, but cried
Like a babe without its corals,
For he knew how hard it is apt to go
When the law and a thief have quarrels, –
There was not a Christian soul alive
To speak a word for his morals.

Oh, how gaily I doff'd my costly gear,
And put on my work-day clothes;
I was tired of such a long Sunday life, –
And never was one of the sloths;
But the beggar man grumbled a weary deal,
And made many crooked mouths.

So I haul'd him off to the gallows' foot,
And blinded him in his bags;
'Twas a weary job to heave him up,
For a doom'd man always lags;
But by ten of the clock he was off his legs
In the wind and airing his rags!

So there he hung and there I stood,
The LAST MAN left alive,
To have my own will of all the earth:
Quoth I, now I shall thrive!
But when was ever honey made
With one bee in a hive!

My conscience began to gnaw my heart,
Before the day was done,
For the other men's lives had all gone out,
Like candles in the sun! –
But it seem'd as if I had broke, at last,
A thousand necks in one!

So I went and cut his body down,
To bury it decentlie; --
God send there were any good soul alive
To do the like by me!
But the wild dogs came with terrible speed,
And bay'd me up the tree!

My sight was like a drunkard's sight,
And my head began to swim,
To see their jaws all white with foam,
Like the ravenous ocean-brim; –
But when the wild dogs trotted away
Their jaws were bloody and grim!

Their jaws were bloody and grim, good Lord!
But the beggar man, where was he? –
There was nought of him but some ribbons of rags
Below the gallows' tree! –
I know the Devil, when I am dead,
Will send his hounds for me! –

I've buried my babies one by one,
And dug the deep hole for Joan,
And cover'd the faces of kith and kin,
And felt the old churchyard stone
Go cold to my heart, full many a time,
But I never felt so lone!

For the lion and Adam were company,
And the tiger him beguil'd;
But the simple kine are foes to my life,
And the household brutes are wild.
If the veriest cur would lick my hand,
I could love it like a child!

And the beggar man's ghost besets my dream,
At night, to make me madder, –
And my wretched conscience, within my breast,
Is like a stinging adder; –
I sigh when I pass the gallows' foot,
And look at the rope and ladder!

For hanging looks sweet, – but, alas! in vain,
My desperate fancy begs, –
I must turn my cup of sorrows quite up,
And drink it to the dregs, –
For there's not another man alive,
In the world, to pull my legs!

THOMAS HOOD

66 Beyond Words

That row of icicles along the gutter
Feels like my armoury of hate;
And you, you . . . you, you utter . . .
You wait.

ROBERT FROST

67 An Answer to the Parson

'Why of the sheep do you not learn peace?'
'Because I don't want you to shear my fleece.'

WILLIAM BLAKE

68 Fragment

as for him who
finds fault
may silliness

and sorrow
overtake him
when you wrote

you did not
know
the power of

your words.

WILLIAM CARLOS WILLIAMS

69 A Poison Tree

I was angry with my friend :
I told my wrath, my wrath did end.
I was angry with my foe :
I told it not, my wrath did grow.

And I water'd it in fears,
Night and morning with my tears ;
And I sunnèd it with smiles,
And with soft deceitful wiles.

And it grew both day and night,
Till it bore an apple bright ;
And my foe beheld it shine,
And he knew that it was mine,

And into my garden stole
When the night had veil'd the pole :
In the morning glad I see
My foe outstretch'd beneath the tree.

WILLIAM BLAKE

70 False Friends-Like

When I wer still a bwoy, an' mother's pride,
A bigger bwoy spoke up to me so kind-like,
'If you do like, I'll treat ye wi' a ride
On theäse wheel-barrow here.' Zoo I wer blind-like
To what he had a-workèn in his mind-like,
An' mounted vor a passenger inside ;
An' comèn to a puddle, perty wide,
He tipp'd me in, a-grinnèn back behind-like.
Zoo when a man do come to me so thick-like,
An' sheäke my hand, where woonce he pass'd me by,
An' tell me he would do me this or that,
I can't help thinkèn o' the big bwoy's trick-like.
An' then, vor all I can but wag my hat
An' thank en, I do veel a little shy.

WILLIAM BARNES

71 Traveller's Curse After Misdirection

(From the Welsh)

May they stumble, stage by stage
On an endless pilgrimage,
Dawn and dusk, mile after mile,
At each and every step, a stile;
At each and every step withal
May they catch their feet and fall;
At each and every fall they take
May a bone within them break;
And may the bone that breaks within
Not be, for variation's sake,
Now rib, now thigh, now arm, now shin,
But always, without fail, THE NECK.

ROBERT GRAVES

72 Fragment XXXII

A flea whose body shone like bead
Gave me delight as I gave heed.

A spider whose legs like stiff thread
Made me think quaintly as I read.

A rat whose droll shape would dart and flit
Was like a torch to light my wit.

A fool whose narrow forehead hung
A wooden target for my tongue.

A meagre wretch in whose generous scum
Himself was lost – his $\begin{Bmatrix} \text{dirty} \\ \text{living} \end{Bmatrix}$ tomb.

But the flea crawled too near –
His blood the smattered wall doth smear.

And the spider being too brave
No doctor now can him save.

And when the rat would rape my cheese
He signed the end of his life's lease.

O cockney who maketh negatives,
You negative of negatives.

1914

ISAAC ROSENBERG

73 The End of the World

Quite unexpectedly as Vasserot
The armless ambidextrian was lighting
A match between his great and second toe
And Ralph the lion was engaged in biting
The neck of Madame Sossman while the drum
Pointed, and Teeny was about to cough
In waltz-time swinging Jocko by the thumb –
Quite unexpectedly the top blew off:

And there, there overhead, there, there, hung over
Those thousands of white faces, those dazed eyes,
There in the starless dark, the poise, the hover,
There with vast wings across the cancelled skies,
There in the sudden blackness the black pall
Of nothing, nothing, nothing – nothing at all.

ARCHIBALD McLEISH

74 Latter-Day Geography Lesson

This, quoth the Eskimo master,
        was London in English times:
        step out a little bit faster
        you two young men at the last there
        the Bridge would be on our right hand
        and the Tower near where those crows stand –
        we struck it you'll recall in Gray's rhymes:
        this, quoth the Eskimo master,
        was London in English times.

This, quoth the Eskimo master,
    was London in English days :
    beyond that hill they called Clapham
    boys that swear Master Redtooth I slap 'em
    I dis-tinct-ly heard – you – say – Bastard
    don't argue : here boys, ere disaster
    overtook her, in splendour there lay
    a city held empires in sway
    and filled all the earth with her praise :
    this, quoth the Eskimo master,
    was London in English days.

She held, quoth the Eskimo master,
    ten million when her prime was full
    from here once Britannia cast her
    gaze over an Empire vaster
    even than ours : look there Woking
    stood, I make out, and the Abbey
    lies here under our feet *you great babby*
    Swift-and-short do – please – kindly – stop – poking
    your thumbs through the eyes of that skull.

R. A. K. MASON

75 Fifteen

Seventeenth Street

South of the bridge on Seventeenth
I found back of the willows one summer
day a motorcycle with engine running
as it lay on its side, ticking over
slowly in the high grass. I was fifteen.

I admired all that pulsing gleam, the
shiny flanks, the demure headlights
fringed where it lay ; I led it gently
to the road and stood with that
companion, ready and friendly. I was fifteen.

We could find the end of a road, meet
the sky on out Seventeenth. I thought about
hills, and patting the handle got back a
confident opinion. On the bridge we indulged
a forward feeling, a tremble. I was fifteen.

Thinking, back farther in the grass I found
the owner, just coming to, where he had flipped
over the rail. He had blood on his hand, was pale –
I helped him walk to his machine. He ran his hand
over it, called me good man, roared away.

I stood there, fifteen.

WILLIAM STAFFORD

76 Timothy Winters

Timothy Winters comes to school
With eyes as wide as a football-pool,
Ears like bombs and teeth like splinters :
A blitz of a boy is Timothy Winters.

His belly is white, his neck is dark,
And his hair is an exclamation-mark.
His clothes are enough to scare a crow
And through his britches the blue winds blow.

When teacher talks he won't hear a word
And he shoots down dead the arithmetic-bird,
He licks the patterns off his plate
And he's not even heard of the Welfare State.

Timothy Winters has bloody feet
And he lives in a house on Suez Street,
He sleeps in a sack on the kitchen floor
And they say there aren't boys like him any more.

Old Man Winters likes his beer
And his missus ran off with a bombardier,
Grandma sits in the grate with a gin
And Timothy's dosed with an aspirin.

The Welfare Worker lies awake
But the law's as tricky as a ten-foot snake,
So Timothy Winters drinks his cup
And slowly goes on growing up.

prays At Morning Prayers the Master helves
for children less fortunate than ourselves,
And the loudest response in the room is when
Timothy Winters roars 'Amen!'

So come one angel, come on ten :
Timothy Winters says 'Amen
Amen amen amen amen.'
Timothy Winters, Lord.
                              Amen.

CHARLES CAUSLEY

77 Our Father

She said my father had whiskers and looked like God ;
that he swore like a fettler, drank like a bottle ;
used to run away from mother, left money for food ;
called us by numbers ; had a belt with a buckle.

On Sunday was churchday. We children walked behind.
He'd wear a stiff collar. He'd say good-morning.
And we made jokes about him, we were afraid
because already we understood about hating.

When we'd left the church that was so nice and still,
the minister would let us give the bells a telling –
four dong-dells ; and we'd decide that Nell's
was to be the end of the world ; it was time for going.

When we got home he'd take off his collar, and his shoes ;
and his Sunday-special braces ; and we'd whisper,
he's not like God. So that he'd belt us for the noise,
and we'd yell. And on Mondays he'd run away from mother.

RAY MATHEW

78 Brother

It's odd enough to be alive with others,
But odder still to have sisters and brothers:
To make one of a characteristic litter –
The sisters puzzled and vexed, the brothers vexed and bitter
That this one wears, though flattened by abuse,
The family nose for individual use.

ROBERT GRAVES

79 Heredity

I am the family face;
Flesh perishes, I live on,
Projecting trait and trace
Through time to times anon,
And leaping from place to place
Over oblivion.

The years-heired feature that can
In curve and voice and eye
Despise the human span
Of durance – that is I;
The eternal thing in man,
That heeds no call to die.

THOMAS HARDY

80 Phizzog

This face you got,
This here phizzog you carry around,
You never picked it out for yourself, at all, at all – did you?
This here phizzog – somebody handed it to you – am I right?
Somebody said, 'Here's yours, now go see what you can do
  with it.'
Somebody slipped it to you and it was like a package marked:
'No goods exchanged after being taken away ' –
This face you got.

CARL SANDBURG

81 Ages of Man

1   As foolish as monkeys till twenty or more;
    As bold as lions till forty and four;
    As cunning as foxes till three score and ten;
    Then they become asses or something – not men.

2   At ten a child; at twenty wild;
    At thirty tame if ever;
    At forty wise, at fifty rich;
    At sixty good, or never.

TRADITIONAL

82 Blaming Sons

An Apology for his own Drunkenness, A.D. *406*

White hairs cover my temples,
I am wrinkled and gnarled beyond repair,
And though I have got five sons,
They all hate paper and brush.
A-shu is eighteen:
For laziness there is none like him.
A-hsüan does his best,
But really loathes the Fine Arts.
Yung and Tuan are thirteen,
But do not know 'six' from 'seven'.
T'ung-tzu in his ninth year
Is only concerned with things to eat.
If Heaven treats me like this,
What can I do but fill my cup?

T'AO CH'IEN Translated from the Chinese by Arthur Waley

83 A Right Carry-On

When I was a chicken as big as a hen,
My mother hit me, and I hit her again;
My father came in, and said what're yer 'bout?
So I up with my fist, and I gin him a clout.

TRADITIONAL

84 Adolescent

A chap be called a hobble-de-hoye,
As be short of a man, but moor'n a boy.

TRADITIONAL

85 Parents and Children

As tall as your knee, they are pretty to see;
As tall as your head, they wish you were dead.

TRADITIONAL

86 Sauce for the Goose . . .

'Now, dearest Fred,' she softly said,
'You must abandon smoking;
It spoils your looks – and then your breath –
Indeed it's most provoking.
Did God decree that man should be
A chimney flue regarded?
Then, darling Fred, let it be said,
Tobacco you've discarded.'

'Haw, well, my dear,' said Fred, 'I fear
That will not be so easy,
But like a man I'll try a plan,
And do the best to please ye.
Did God intend that woman's mind
Such wondrous things should brew, love,
As bustles, bloomers, crinolines,
Or Hoops-de-dooden-do, love?
But really, if' – wif, wif, wif, wif –
'And mind you, I'm not joking –
If you abandon crinoline,
By Jove; I – I'll give up smoking.'

ANONYMOUS

V₂—D

87 I Play it Cool

I play it cool and dig all jive.
That's the reason I stay alive.
My motto, as I live and learn,
Is : Dig and Be Dug in Return.

LANGSTON HUGHES

88 In My Host's Garden

'Don't break it !' he said,
    then broke off and gave me
    a branch of his plum.

TAIGI Translated from the Japanese by Harold G. Henderson

89 To Know Whom One Shall Marry

You must lie in another county, and knit the left garter
about the right legged stocking (let the other garter and
stocking alone) and as you rehearse these following verses,
at every comma knit a knot.

This knot I knit,
To know the thing, I know not yet,
That I may see,
The man that shall my husband be,
How he goes, and what he wears,
And what he does, all days, and years.

TRADITIONAL

90 When to Cut Your Nails

A man had better ne'er been born,
Than have his nails on Sunday shorn.
Cut them on Monday,
Cut them for health ;
Cut them on Tuesday,
Cut them for wealth ;
Cut them on Wednesday,
Cut them for news ;
Cut them on Thursday,
A new pair of shoes ;
Cut them on Friday,
Cut them for sorrow ;
Cut them on Saturday,
See your sweetheart tomorrow.

TRADITIONAL

91 Who ? What ?

He that loves Glass without a G,
Take away L and that is he.

TRADITIONAL

92 Conversation-Piece

Old woman, old woman, wilt thee gang a-shearin' ?
Speak a little louder, I am very hard o' hearin' !
Old woman, old woman, wilt thee gang a-gleanin' ?
Speak a little louder, or what's the use o' tawkin'.
Old woman, old woman, wilt thee let me kiss thee ?
Yes, kind sir, and the Lord i' heav'n bless thee.

TRADITIONAL

93 How Much ?

How much do you love me, a million bushels ?
Oh, a lot more than that. Oh, a lot more.

And tomorrow maybe only half a bushel ?
Tomorrow maybe not even a half a bushel.

And is this your heart arithmetic ?
This is the way the wind measures the weather.

CARL SANDBURG

94 Girl, Boy, Flower, Bicycle

This girl
Waits at the corner for
This boy
Freewheeling on his bicycle.
She holds
A flower in her hand
A gold flower
In her hands she holds
The sun.
With power between his thighs
The boy
Comes smiling to her
He rides
A bicycle that glitters like
The wind.
This boy this girl
They walk
In step with the wind
Arm in arm
They climb the level street
To where
Laid on the glittering handlebars
The flower
Is round and shining as
The sun.

M. K. JOSEPH

95 A Charme, or an Allay for Love

If so be a Toad be laid
In a Sheeps-skin newly flaid,
And that ty'd to man, 'twil sever
Him and his affections ever.

ROBERT HERRICK

96 Short Poem

You slapped my face
oh but so gently
I smiled
at the caress.

WILLIAM CARLOS WILLIAMS

97 The Night-Piece to Julia

Her Eyes the Glow-worme lend thee,
The Shooting Starres attend thee;
    And the Elves also,
    Whose little eyes glow,
Like the sparks of fire, befriend thee.

No *Will-o'th'-Wispe* mis-light thee;
Nor Snake, or Slow-worms bite thee:
    But on, on thy way
    Not making a stay,
Since Ghost ther's none to affright thee.

Let not the darke thee cumber;
What though the Moon do's slumber?
    The Starres of the night
    Will lend thee their light,
Like Tapers cleare without number.

Then *Julia* let me wooe thee,
Thus, thus to come unto me:

And when I shall meet
Thy silv'ry feet,
My soule Ile poure into thee.

ROBERT HERRICK

98   The Crow Sat on the Willow

The Crow sat on the willow tree
A lifting up his wings
And glossy was his coat to see
And loud the ploughman sings
I love my love because I know
The milkmaid she loves me
And hoarsely croaked the glossy crow
Upon the willow tree
I love my love the ploughman sung
And all the field wi' music rung

I love my love a bonny lass
She keeps her pails so bright
And blythe she trips the dewy grass
At morning and at night
A cotton drab her morning gown
Her face was rosey health
She traced the pastures up and down
And nature was her wealth
He sung and turned each furrow down
His sweethearts love in cotton gown

My love is young and handsome
As any in the Town
She's worth a Ploughman's ransom
In the drab cotton gown
He sung and turned his furrows o'er
And urged his Team along
While on the willow as before
The old crow croaked his song
The ploughman sung his rustic Lay
And sung of Phebe all the day

The crow he was in love no doubt
And wi' a many things
The ploughman finished many a bout
And lustily he sings
My love she is a milking maid
Wi' red and rosey cheek
O' cotton drab her gown was made
I loved her many a week
His milking maid the ploughman sung
Till all the fields around him rung

JOHN CLARE

99 Song

I wish I was where I would be
With love alone to dwell
Was I but her or she but me
Then love would all be well
I wish to send my thoughts to her
As quick as thoughts can fly
But as the wind the waters stir
The mirrors change and flye

JOHN CLARE

100 Song

<small>until</small> I hid my love when young while I
Couldn't bear the buzzing of a flye
I hid my love to my despite
Till I could not bear to look at light
I dare not gaze upon her face
But left her memory in each place
Where ere I saw a wild flower lye
I kissed and bade my love good bye

I met her in the greenest dells
Where dew drops pearl the wood blue bells
The lost breeze kissed her bright blue eye
The bee kissed and went stinging bye

A sun beam found a passage there
A gold chain round her neck so fair
As secret as the wild bees song
She lay there all the summer long

I hid my love in field and town
Till e'en the breeze would knock me down
The Bees seemed singing ballads o'er
The flyes buss turned a Lion's roar
And even silence found a tongue
To haunt me all the summer long
The riddle nature could not prove
Was nothing else but secret love

JOHN CLARE

101 Scarborough Fair

Are you going to Scarborough Fair?
Parsley, Sage, Rosemary and Thyme.
Remember me to one who lived there,
For once she was a true love of mine.

Tell her to make me a cambric shirt –
Parsley, Sage, Rosemary and Thyme –
Without any seam or needlework.
She shall be a true love of mine.

Tell her to wash it in yonder dry well –
Parsley, Sage, Rosemary and Thyme –
Where water ne'er sprung nor drop of rain fell.
She shall be a true love of mine.

Tell her to dry it on yonder thorn –
Parsley, Sage, Rosemary and Thyme –
Where blossom ne'er grew since Adam was born.
She shall be a true love of mine.

Well, will you find me an acre of land –
Parsley, Sage, Rosemary and Thyme –
Between the sea foam and the sea sand?
You shall be a true love of mine.

And will you plough it with a lamb's horn –
Parsley, Sage, Rosemary and Thyme –
And sow it all over with one peppercorn?
And you shall be a true love of mine.

Will you reap it with a sickle of leather –
Parsley, Sage, Rosemary and Thyme –
And tie it all up with a peacock's feather?
And you shall be a true love of mine.

And when you've done and you've finished your work –
Parsley, Sage, Rosemary and Thyme –
Then come to me for your cambric shirt,
And you shall be a true love of mine.

TRADITIONAL

102 Song

O wert thou in the storm
  How I would shield thee:
To keep thee dry and warm,
  A camp I would build thee.

Though the clouds pour'd again,
  Not a drop should harm thee,
The music of wind, and rain,
  Rather should charm thee.

O wert thou in the storm,
  A shed I would build thee;
To keep thee dry and warm, –
  How I would shield thee.

The rain should not wet thee,
  Nor thunder clap harm thee.
By thy side I would sit me, –
  To comfort, and warm thee.

I would sit by thy side, love,
  While the dread storm was over; –
And the wings of an angel
  My charmer would cover.

JOHN CLARE

103 Elizabethan Sailor's Song

My love my love is a green box-tree
    And the scarlet hawthorn berry
Give me five cocky starlings on a grass-grown sea
    And a lute to be merry.

Then shall we wander in star-sewn meadows
    Frosted by ancient October
Where ice like iron rims the shadows
    And never be sober.

O what is the brightness behind her eye?
    O let me taste her sweet mouth, begin,
As under the sky we freezing lie
    Cold it is out but not within.

O cease your singing my darling my swallow
    And put away your brown fiddle
For the ship is a-sailing and you cannot follow
    And I have the middle.

middle-watch,
12 to 4 a.m.

CHARLES CAUSLEY

104 O Lurcher-Loving Collier

O lurcher-loving collier, black as night,
Follow your love across the smokeless hill;
Your lamp is out and all the cages still;
Course for her heart and do not miss,
For Sunday soon is past and, Kate, fly not so fast,
For Monday comes when none may kiss:
Be marble to his soot, and to his black be white.

W. H. AUDEN

105 Crime Story

Oh read me this riddle and read it aright,
Where was I last Saturday night?
The wind blew, the cock crew,
I waited for one, and there came two,
The woods did tremble, the boughs did shake,
To see the hole the fox did make;
Too little for a horse, too big for a bee,
I saw it was a hole just a fit for me.

TRADITIONAL

The traditional explanation of this poem is that a girl had
a rendezvous with her false lover: she was early, and saw
him arrive with an accomplice. They then dug her grave.
She presumably slipped away, to live to tell her tale.

106 I Once Went A-Courting

I once went a-courting an old woman's daughter.
She quickly found out what us young 'uns was after.
With arms stuck akimbo in quarrelsome mood,
She swore that she'd settle our loves if she could.
                    (But she couldn't)

  Down, down, derry down day.

She shut to the window and bolted the door,
Then I searched round the cottage behind and before,
And when she popped t'door to, slap bang in my face,
She thought I'd be off and abandon the chase.
                    (But I didn't)

  Down, down, derry down day.

She got an old farmer our wits for to puzzle,
He loaded his blunderbuss up to the muzzle,
And when he presented it close to my head,
It went off with a bang and I thought I was dead.
                    (But I wasn't)

  Down, down, derry down day.

You may think now I didn't go many times more,
Ever courting around this old woman's door.
In singing this ditty, I haven't been long,
You may think there's another long verse to my song.
                              (But there isn't)

  Down, down, derry down day.

TRADITIONAL

107 Last but not Least

The following bill was furnished to a citizen of this metro-
polis some ten or twelve years ago:

  Mr Fullam, Esq.
                    Dr to James Rickard, Shoemaker
  To clicking and sowling Miss Mary   £0   2   2
  To strapping and welting Miss Sally   0   1   4
  To binding and closing Miss Ellen   0   0   8
  To putting a few stitches in Miss Charlotte 0   0   4
                                           £0   4   6*d*

From the *Dublin Comet*, 1831

James Rickard is a shoemaker
Who's sworn he'll never wed
But the daughters of the baker
Are resolved to make his bread.

Miss Mary's to the shoe shop gone
To ask him to click and sowl her.
But for two and two he's not the one
To flatter and console her.

Miss Sally went to Rickard's shop,
Asked him to strap and welt her.
He took his leather strap to strop
That strapping wench and belt her.

Miss Ellen asked James Rickard if
He'd bind and kindly close her.
Said he, 'I'll bind you till you're stiff,
If you come any closer.'

Miss Charlotte wasn't such a fool
And coveting his riches
She placed her foot up on his stool
And he counted all her stitches.

Three greying girls has Mr Fullam –
Three have aching feet.
But Charlotte, not so slow a fool,
Now keeps her shoe shop neat.

JUSTIN ST JOHN

108 The Ballad of Charlotte Dymond

Charlotte Dymond, a domestic servant aged eighteen, was
murdered near Rowtor Ford on Bodmin Moor on Sunday,
14 April 1844, by her young man, a crippled farm-hand,
Matthew Weeks, aged twenty-two. A stone marks the spot.

It was a Sunday evening
   And in the April rain
That Charlotte went from our house
   And never came home again.

Her shawl of diamond redcloth,
   She wore a yellow gown,
She carried the green gauze handkerchief
   She bought in Bodmin town.

About her throat her necklace
   And in her purse her pay:
The four silver shillings
   She had at Lady Day.

In her purse four shillings
   And in her purse her pride
As she walked out one evening
   Her lover at her side.

Out beyond the marshes
   Where the cattle stand,
With her crippled lover
   Limping at her hand.

Charlotte walked with Matthew
  Through the Sunday mist,
Never saw the razor
  Waiting at his wrist.

Charlotte she was gentle
  But they found her in the flood
Her Sunday beads among the reeds
  Beaming with her blood.

Matthew, where is Charlotte,
  And wherefore has she flown?
For you walked out together
  And now are come alone.

Why do you not answer,
  Stand silent as a tree,
Your Sunday worsted stockings
  All muddied to the knee?

Why do you mend your breast-pleat
  With a rusty needle's thread
And fall with fears and silent tears
  Upon your single bed?

Why do you sit so sadly
  Your face the colour of clay
And with a green gauze handkerchief
  Wipe the sour sweat away?

Has she gone to Blisland
  To seek an easier place,
And is that why your eye won't dry
  And blinds your bleaching face?

'Take me home!' cried Charlotte,
  'I lie here in the pit!
A red rock rests upon my breasts
  And my naked neck is split!'

Her skin was soft as sable,
  Her eyes were wide as day,
Her hair was blacker than the bog
  That licked her life away.

Her cheeks were made of honey,
   Her throat was made of flame
Where all around the razor
   Had written its red name.

As Matthew turned at Plymouth
   About the tilting Hoe,
The cold and cunning Constable
   Up to him did go:

'I've come to take you, Matthew,
   Unto the Magistrate's door.
Come quiet now, you pretty poor boy,
   And you must know what for.'

'She is as pure,' cried Matthew,
   'As is the early dew,
Her only stain it is the pain
   That round her neck I drew!

'She is as guiltless as the day
   She sprang forth from her mother.
The only sin upon her skin
   Is that she loved another.'

They took him off to Bodmin,
   They pulled the prison bell,
They sent him smartly up to Heaven
   And dropped him down to Hell.

All through the granite kingdom
   And on its travelling airs
Ask which of these two lovers
   The most deserves your prayers.

And your steel heart search, Stranger,
   That you may pause and pray
For lovers who come not to bed
   Upon their wedding day,

But lie upon the moorland
   Where stands the sacred snow
Above the breathing river,
   And the salt sea-winds go.

CHARLES CAUSLEY

109 The Great Silkie of Sule Skerrie

Seal

In Norway there sits a maid:
'By-loo, my baby,' she begins,
'Little know I my child's father
Or if land or sea he's living in.'

Then there arose at her bed feet,
And a grumly guest I'm sure it was he,
Saying 'Here am I, thy child's father,
Although that I am not comely.

'I am a man upon the land,
I am a silkie in the sea,
And when I am in my own country,
My dwelling is in Sule Skerrie.'

Then he hath taken a purse of gold,
He hath put it upon her knee,
Saying 'Give to me my little wee son,
And take thee up thy nurse's fee.

'And it shall come to pass on a summer day,
When the sun shines hot on every stone,
That I shall take my little wee son,
And I'll teach him for to swim in the foam

'And you will marry a gunner good
And a proud good gunner I'm sure he'll be.
And he'll go out on a May morning
And he'll kill both my wee son and me.'

And lo, she did marry a gunner good,
And a proud good gunner I'm sure it was he;
And the very first shot that e'er he did shoot
He killed the son and the great silkie.

In Norway there sits a maid:
'By-loo, my baby,' she begins,
'Little know I my child's father
Or if land or sea he's living in.'

TRADITIONAL

The IDLE 'PREN

Proverbs
When fear cometh
destruction comet
distress cometh u
call upon God, e

Design'd & Engrav'd by Wᵐ Hogarth

The last dying Speech & Confession of Tho. Idle.

Verf: 27, 28.
...on, and their
...rlwind: when
...hen they shall
...not answer.

Publish'd according to Act of Parliam! Sep: 30. 17.47

110 The Sorrowful Lamentation, Confession and Last Farewell to the World, of John Lomas

Who was executed at Chester, on Monday, the 24th of August, 1812, for the Wilful Murder of Mr George Morrey, of Hankelow, near Nantwich, in the County of Chester, on Sunday Morning, 12th April, 1812.

May my fate be a warning to sinful men, whereby they may forsake their evil ways, and search after righteousness. May the words of a dying man persuade them to this glorious effort, that they may be convinced of its necessity, in order to secure for themselves peace in this world, and everlasting felicity in the world to come. Happy would my end have been had I followed this conduct: shame and terror is my reward for departing from it.

Good people all I pray attend,
Unto these lines which here is penn'd;
A cruel murder I did commit,
And now I do repent of it.

I had a master very kind,
But my mistress on me did set her mind;
And she did teaze me night and day
To take his precious life away.

Soon unto her I did consent
On murder I was fully bent,
For she told me in a little space
I should be happy in his place.

My master had some liquor got,
Not knowing of our wicked plot;
To bed he went, did sleep and snore
Not thinking he should rise no more.

My mistress found he was asleep,
Then from her room did softly creep,
And she did come to my bed side,
To kill him now's the time she cry'd.

Three times I struck him on the head,
And thought he surely had been dead,
But he did spring out on the floor,
Which much surprised us to be sure.

My mistress by me she did stand,
All with a razor in her hand,
Take this, says she, and end his life
And I will be your loving wife.

I cut his throat immediately,
And out the crimson blood did fly
All over me and on the floor,
The scene was awful to be sure.

Then to my room I did return,
My conscience did like fuel burn ;
My crime was of so deep a dye
That murder did for vengeance cry.

Immediately now as you see
I was proved the murderer for to be ;
For with his blood my shirt was dy'd,
A truth that could not be deny'd.

To Chester Gaol then I was ta'en,
In heavy irons to remain,
In dismal cell so very strong,
Till the assizes come on.

When at the bar I did appear
The evidence it was so clear,
The jury all did guilty cry
And I was soon condemned to die.

John Lomas now it is my name,
From Audlem Green, in Cheshire came ;
At twenty years old you see
I come to die on the fatal tree.

May young and old a warning take,
And think on my untimely fate !
Here you may see the offence and crime,
For which I suffer in my prime.

ANONYMOUS BROADSHEET BALLAD

111 A Gentleman

'He has robbed two clubs. The judge at Salisbury
Can't give him more than he undoubtedly
Deserves. The scoundrel ! Look at his photograph !
A lady-killer ! Hanging's too good by half
For such as he.' So said the stranger, one
With crimes yet undiscovered or undone.
But at the inn the Gipsy dame began :
'Now he was what I call a gentleman.
He went along with Carrie, and when she
Had a baby he paid up so readily
His half a crown. Just like him. A crown'd have been
More like him. For I never knew him mean.
Oh ! but he was such a nice gentleman. Oh !
Last time we met he said if me and Joe
Was anywhere near we must be sure and call.
He put his arms around our Amos all
As if he were his own son. I pray God
Save him from justice ! Nicer man never trod.'

EDWARD THOMAS

112 Cowboys

Panther-footed saunter in the street,
Who spinning six blunt sounds in the mouth's chamber
Tongue-hammer them one by one when they meet.

Evening. Eyes sharpen under sombre
Brims, drilling the distance for a spurt of hooves.
These wait only for the Stage to lumber

Between sights, to squander their nine lives
(In a town now dead from the waist up,
For where are the children and the shopping wives ?)

They saunter with slack hands, but at the drop
Of a card will conjure guns out of thick air –
Explode every bottle on the bar-top –

Eclipse the lamp with a shooting star –
Struggle under tables, until the one
With the grin knock senseless the one with the scar.

Justice done and seen to be done,
A bullet in front for one in the back,
The honest stranger on the white stallion

Canters off singing. Shopkeeper and clerk
Lunge to their panther feet in the one-and-nines,
Saunter slack-handed into the dark,

And manfully ride home their bucking trains:
Each wearing, like a medal, his chosen wound
To cancel the reproach of varicose veins.

JON STALLWORTHY

113 On the Swag

His body doubled
    under the pack
    that sprawls untidily
    on his old back
    the cold wet deadbeat
    plods up the track.

The cook peers out:
    'oh curse that old lag
    here again
    with his clumsy swag
    made of a dirty old
    turnip-bag.'

'Bring him in, cook,
    from the grey level sleet,
    put silk on his body,
    slippers on his feet,
    give him fire
    and bread and meat,

'Let the fruit be plucked
    and the cake be iced,
    the bed be snug
    and the wine be spiced
    in the old cove's nightcap :
    for this is Christ.'

R. A. K. MASON

114 The Dead Swagman

His rusted billy left beside the tree ;
Under a root, most carefully tucked away,
His steel-rimmed glasses folded in their case
Of mildewed purple velvet ; there he lies
In the sunny afternoon, and takes his ease,
Curled like a possum within the hollow trunk.

He came one winter evening when the tree
Hunched its broad back against the rain, and made
His camp, and slept, and did not wake again.
Now white-ants make a home within his skull :
His old friend Fire has walked across the hill
And blackened the old tree and the old man
And buried him half in ashes, where he lay.

It might be called a lonely death. The tree
Led its own alien life beneath the sun,
Yet both belonged to the Bush, and now are one :
The roots and bones lie close among the soil,
And he ascends in leaves towards the sky.

NANCY CATO

115 A Civil Servant

While in this cavernous place employed
  Not once was I aware
Of my officious other-self
  Poised high above me there,

My self reversed, my rage-less part,
  A slimy yellowish cone –
Drip, drip ; drip, drip – so down the years
  I stalagmized in stone.

Now pilgrims to the cave, who come
  To chip off what they can,
Prod me with child-like merriment :
  'Look, look ! It's like a man ! '

ROBERT GRAVES

116 Reuben Bright

Because he was a butcher and thereby
Did earn an honest living (and did right)
I would not have you think that Reuben Bright
Was any more a brute than you or I ;
For when they told him that his wife must die,
He stared at them and shook with grief and fright,
And cried like a great baby half that night,
And made the women cry to see him cry.

And after she was dead, and he had paid
The singers and sexton and the rest,
He packed a lot of things that she had made
Most mournfully away in an old chest
Of hers, and put some chopped-up cedar boughs
In with them, and tore down the slaughter-house.

EDWIN ARLINGTON ROBINSON

117 Riches

When I wish I was rich, then I know I am ill.
Because, to tell the truth, I have enough as I am.
So when I catch myself thinking : Ah, if I was rich - !
I say to myself: Hello ! I'm not well. My vitality is low.

D. H. LAWRENCE

118 Willy Wet-Leg

I can't stand Willy wet-leg,
can't stand him at any price.
He's resigned, and when you hit him
he lets you hit him twice.

D. H. LAWRENCE

119 A Negro Woman

carrying a bunch of marigolds
        wrapped
                in an old newspaper :
She carries them upright,
        bareheaded,
                the bulk
of her thighs
        causing her to waddle
                as she walks
looking into
        the store window which she passes
                on her way.
What is she
        but an ambassador
                from another world
a world of pretty marigolds
        of two shades
                which she announces

not knowing what she does
    other
            than walk the streets
holding the flowers upright
    as a torch
            so early in the morning.

WILLIAM CARLOS WILLIAMS

120 First of the Migrants

First of the migrants, overnight they say
Naz flew to London. She will glide no more
Vivid as a rainbow through this door
With her sketch-book under an arm. Today,
Missing her small step, one imagines
The rainbow sari in a Georgian square
Painting the wind ; bus-queues turning to stare
At a bird of Paradise among pigeons.

JON STALLWORTHY

121 Old Florist

That hump of a man bunching chrysanthemums
Or pinching-back asters, or planting azaleas,
Tamping and stamping dirt into pots –
How he could flick and pick
Rotten leaves or yellowy petals,
Or scoop out a weed close to flourishing roots,
Or make the dust buzz with a light spray,
Or drown a bug in one spit of tobacco juice,
Or fan life into wilted sweet-peas with his hat,
Or stand all night watering roses, his feet blue in rubber boots.

THEODORE ROETHKE

122 Old Man at Valdez

No books, no songs
belong in the eighty-
year old memory:
he knows where
the Indian graves are
in the woods, recalls
the day the Apaches
crept into Valdez
carrying away
a boy who
forty years later
came back
lacking one arm and said:
'I could hear you all
searching, but I
dursn't cry out
for fear they'd . . .'
The Indians
had trained their prize
to be a one-armed thief.
'And we never did,' the old man says,
'see a thief like him
in Valdez.'

New Mexico

CHARLES TOMLINSON

123 The River Crossing

The river was announcing
An ominous crossing
With the boulders knocking.

'You can do it and make a fight of it,
Always taking the hard way
For the hell and delight of it.

'But there comes the day
When you watch the spate of it,
And camp till the moon's down
– Then find the easy way
Across in the dawn,
Waiting till that swollen vein
Of a river subsides again.'

And Bill set up his camp and watched
His young self, river-cold and scratched,
Struggling across, and up the wrong ridge,
And turning back, temper on edge.

DENIS GLOVER

124 Johnny Armstrong

There dwelt a man in fair Westmoreland,
Johnny Armstrong men did him call,
He had neither lands nor rents coming in,
Yet he kept eight score men in his hall.

He had horse and harness for them all,
Goodly steeds were all milk-white;
O the golden bands about their necks,
And their weapons, they were all alike.

News then was brought unto the king
That there was such a one as he,
That lived like a bold outlaw
And robbed all the North country.

The king he wrote a letter then,
A letter which was large and long;
He signed it with his own hand,
And he promised to do him no wrong.

When this letter came to Johnny,
His heart it was as blythe as birds on the tree.
'Never was I sent for before any king,
My father, my grandfather, nor none but me.

'And if we go before the king
I would we went most orderly;
Every man of you shall have his scarlet cloak,
Laced with silver laces three.

'Every one of you shall have his velvet coat,
Laced with silver lace so white;
O the golden bands about your necks,
Black hats, white feathers, all alike.'

By the morrow morning at ten of the clock,
Towards Edinburgh gone was he,
And with him all his eight score men;
Good lord, it was a goodly sight for to see!

When Johnny came before the king,
He fell down on his knee,
'O pardon, my sovereign liege,' he said,
'O pardon my eight score men and me!'

'Thou shalt have no pardon, thou traitor strong,
For thy eight score men nor thee;
For tomorrow morning by ten of the clock,
Both thou and them shall hang on the gallow-tree.'

But Johnny looked over his left shoulder,
Good lord, what a grievous look looked he!
Saying, 'Asking grace of a graceless face –
Why there is none for you nor me.'

But Johnny had a bright sword by his side,
And it was made of the metal so free,
That had not the king stept his foot aside,
He had smitten his head from his fair body,

Saying, 'Fight on, my merry men all,
And see that none of you be ta'en;
For rather than men shall say we were hanged,
Let them report how we were slain.'

Then, God knows, fair Edinburgh rose,
And so beset poor Johnny round,
That fourscore and ten of Johnny's best men
Lay gasping all upon the ground.

V2—E

Then like a mad man Johnny laid about,
And like a mad man then fought he,
Until a false Scot came Johnny behind
And ran him through the fair body,

Saying, 'Fight on, my merry men all,
And see that none of you be ta'en;
For I will stand by and bleed but awhile,
And then will I come and fight again.'

News then was brought to young Johnny Armstrong,
As he stood by his nurse's knee,
Who vowed if e'er he lived for to be a man,
Of the treacherous Scots revenged he'd be.

TRADITIONAL

125 Saint

This Blatant Beast was finally overcome
And in no secret tourney: wit and fashion
Flocked out and for compassion
Wept as the Red Cross Knight pushed the blade home.

The people danced and sang the paeans due,
Roasting whole oxen on the public spit;
Twelve mountain peaks were lit
With bonfires; yet their hearts were doubt and rue.

Therefore no grave was deep enough to hold
The Beast, who after days came thrusting out,
Wormy from rump to snout,
His yellow cere-cloth patched with the grave's mould.

Nor could sea hold him: anchored with huge rocks,
He swelled and buoyed them up, paddling ashore
As evident as before
With deep-sea ooze and salty creaking bones.

Lime could not burn him, nor the sulphur fire :
So often as the good Knight bound him there,
With stink of singeing hair
And scorching flesh the corpse rolled from the pyre.

In the city-gutter would the Beast lie
Praising the Knight for all his valorous deeds :
'Ay, on those water-meads
He slew even me. These death-wounds testify.'

The Knight governed that city, a man shamed
And shrunken : for the Beast was over-dead,
With wounds no longer red
But gangrenous and loathsome and inflamed.

Not all the righteous judgements he could utter,
Nor mild laws frame, nor public works repair,
Nor wars wage, in despair,
Could bury that same Beast, crouched in the gutter.

A fresh remembrance-banquet to forestall,
The Knight turned hermit, went without farewell
To a far mountain-cell ;
But the Beast followed as his seneschal,

And there drew water for him and hewed wood
With vacant howling laughter ; else all day
Noisome with long decay
Sunning himself at the cave's entry stood.

Would bawl to pilgrims for a dole of bread
To feed the sick saint who once vanquished him
With spear so stark and grim ;
Would set a pillow of grass beneath his head,
Would fetch him fever-wort from the pool's brim –
And crept into his grave when he was dead.

ROBERT GRAVES

126 Cowboy Song

I come from Salem County
    Where the silver melons grow,
Where the wheat is sweet as an angel's feet
    And the zithering zephyrs blow.
I walk the blue bone-orchard
    In the apple-blossom snow,
When the teasy bees take their honeyed ease
    And the marmalade moon hangs low.

My Maw sleeps prone on the prairie
    In a boulder eiderdown,
Where the pickled stars in their little jam-jars
    Hang in a hoop to town.
I haven't seen Paw since a Sunday
    In eighteen seventy-three
When he packed his snap in a bitty mess-trap
    And said he'd be home by tea.

Fled is my fancy sister
    All weeping like the willow,
And dead is the brother I loved like no other
    Who once did share my pillow.
I fly the florid water
    Where run the seven geese round,
O the townsfolk talk to see me walk
    Six inches off the ground.

Across the map of midnight
    I trawl the turning sky,
In my green glass the salt fleets pass
    The moon her fire-float by.
The girls go gay in the valley
    When the boys come down from the farm,
Don't run, my joy, from a poor cowboy,
    I won't do you no harm.

The bread of my twentieth birthday
    I buttered with the sun,
Though I sharpen my eyes with lovers' lies
    I'll never see twenty-one.

Light is my shirt with lilies,
  And lined with lead my hood,
On my face as I pass is a plate of brass,
  And my suit is made of wood.

CHARLES CAUSLEY

127 John Randall

Where have you been to, John Randall my son?
Where have you been to, my handsome young man?
A hawking and hunting; mother, make my bed soon:
I'm sick at my heart and I fain would lie down.

Where's your hawk and your hound, then, John Randall my
    son?
They're dinnered and dead; mother, make my bed soon:
I'm sick at my heart and I fain would lie down.

What had you for dinner, John Randall my son?
Eels and fresh broth; mother, make my bed soon:
I'm sick at my heart and I fain would lie down.

Of what colour were they, John Randall my son?
Their skins they were spotted; mother, make my bed soon:
I'm sick at my heart and I fain would lie down.

They swam in no river; they basked in the sun
And crawled in hedge-bottoms – O make my bed soon:
I'm sick at my heart; mother, let me lie down.

O then you are poisoned, John Randall my son.
It was my own sweetheart; mother, make my bed soon:
I'm sick at my heart and I fain would lie down.

My hound ate the skins and fell down ere he'd done,
At her door, like a stranger; O make my bed soon:
I'm sick at my heart and am fain to lie down.

My hawk on her hand looked for friends and found none,
Taking poison for kindness; O hear my will soon,
For I'm sick, sad, and weary, and fain to lie down.

What leave you your mother, John Randall my son?
My lands and my livings; mother, make my bed soon:
I'm sick at my heart and I fain would lie down.

What leave you your brother, John Randall my son?
My coach and my horses; mother, make my bed soon:
I'm sick at my heart and I fain would lie down.

What leave you your sweetheart, John Randall my son?
The curse of God, mother. O make my bed soon
For I'm sick at my heart and I fain would lie down.

TRADITIONAL Collected by John Clare

128 The Wind

The Wind – tapped like a tired Man –
And like a Host – 'Come in'
I boldly answered – entered then
My Residence within

A Rapid – footless Guest –
To offer whom a Chair
Were as impossible as hand
A Sofa to the Air –

No Bone had He to bind Him –
His Speech was like the Push
Of numerous Humming Birds at once
From a superior Bush –

His Countenance – a Billow –
His Fingers, as He passed
Let go a music – as of tunes
Blown tremulous in Glass –

He visited – still flitting –
Then like a timid Man
Again, He tapped – 'twas flurriedly –
And I became alone –

EMILY DICKINSON

129 Night Wind

Darkness like midnight from the sobbing woods
Clamours with dismal tidings of the rain
Roaring as rivers breaking loose in floods
To spread and foam and deluge all the plain
cottager   The cotter listens at his door again
Half doubting wether it be floods or wind
And through the thickening darkness looks affraid
Thinking of roads that travel has to find
Through nights black depths in dangers garb arrayed
chattering noise|flare   And the loud glabber round the flaze soon stops
When hushed to silence by the lifted hand
Of fearing dame who hears the noise in dread
And thinks a deluge comes to drown the land
Nor dares she go to bed untill the tempest drops

JOHN CLARE

130 The Bird of Night

A shadow is floating through the moonlight.
Its wings don't make a sound.
Its claws are long, its beak is bright.
Its eyes try all the corners of the night.

It calls and calls: all the air swells and heaves
And washes up and down like water.
The ear that listens to the owl believes
In death. The bat beneath the eaves,

The mouse beside the stone are still as death.
The owl's air washes them like water.
The owl goes back and forth inside the night,
And the night holds its breath.

RANDALL JARRELL

131 Fragment XXIV

The monster wind prowls in the writhen trees,
The wind dives in the writhen trees,
They strain in angered leash their green,
They are only strong in ease.

Soft, forward, inarticulate,
Warm, wayward, drooping, or aburst,
Rushing, it tires, slacks to abate.

The wind wakes in the writhen trees

1914

ISAAC ROSENBERG

132 The North Wind

If one should meet the North Wind in the flesh,
Would he be blustery? I don't think so.
I see in my mind's eye a kind of failure,
Dickensian, mousy, a shuffler, living alone
In a London flat, descending for meals,
Sitting the evenings out in the parlor with puzzles,
Games, talk of the neighbors, belches,
And then padding up to his cold bare room at bedtime
To lie awake in the dark in the windless hours
Muttering, 'Boreas, Boreas, I am Boreas –
D'ye hear?'

REED WHITTEMORE

133 Florida Road Workers

I'm makin' a road
For the cars
To fly by on.
Makin' a road
Through the palmetto thicket
For light and civilization
To travel on.

Makin' a road
For the rich old white men
To sweep over in their big cars
And leave me standin' here.

Sure,
A road helps all of us!
White folks ride –
And I get to see 'em ride.
I ain't never seen nobody
Ride so fine before.
Hey buddy!
Look at me.
I'm making a road!

LANGSTON HUGHES

134 I'm a Navvy

I'm a navvy, you'm a navvy,
Working on the line,
Five-and-twenty bob a week,
And all the overtime.
Roast beef, boiled beef,
Puddings made of eggs;
Up jumps a navvy
With a pair of sausage legs.

TRADITIONAL

135 Manual System

Mary has a thingamajig clamped on her ears
And sits all day taking plugs out and sticking plugs in.
Flashes and flashes – voices and voices calling for ears to
  pour words in
Faces at the ends of wires asking for other faces at the ends
  of other wires :
All day taking plugs out and sticking plugs in,
Mary has a thingamajig clamped on her ears.

CARL SANDBURG

136 On a British Submarine

It happened on a sunny day in nineteen fifty-four.
We went to greet Her Majesty a-coming from the tour.

  On a British submarine, on a British submarine,
  When sixty solid sailors went a-cheering of the Queen.

Their lordships said : Now cheer, m'boys, but mind you make
  it smart,
There's nothing looks so ragged as a-cheering from your heart.

Well when we saw the signal, boys, it made our innards freeze :
On the order ONE, you hold your hats at forty-five degrees.

At forty-five degrees, m'boys, that's what their lordships said :
On the order TWO, you wave your hats three times around your
  heads.

And when you go to shout, m'boys, be careful what you say,
The word you use for cheering is : Hurrah ! and not : Hooray !

We sailed towards the *Brittania*, boys, the finest ever seen
With every man a-standing like a petrified marine.

But when we reached the moment, boys, that every skipper
  dreads,
A swarm of gnats as big as bats descended on our heads.

The boat was filled with waving arms, the air was filled with
cries,
As every matelot cursed and fought to keep them from his eyes.

The Duke he scratched his head as he watched us all depart:
That's the first time I've seen sailor boys a-cheering from their
heart.

We waved our way across the bay till we were out of sight,
We waved our way all through the day and on into the night.

Ah, the day we met the Queen, m'boys, is a day I won't forget,
If we hadn't dived to ninety feet we'd all be waving yet.

CYRIL TAWNEY

137 Send out your Homing Pigeons, Dai

Send out your homing pigeons, Dai,
Your blue-grey pigeons, hard as nails,
Send them with messages tied to their wings,
Words of your anger, words of your love.
Send them to Dover, to Glasgow, to Cork,
Send them to the wharves of Hull and of Belfast,
To the harbours of Liverpool and Dublin and Leith,
Send them to the islands and out of the oceans,
To the wild wet islands of the northern sea
Where little grey women go out in heavy shawls
At the hour of dusk to gaze on the merciless waters,
And send them to the decorated islands of the south
Where the mineowner and his tall stiff lady
Walk round and round the rose-pink hotel, day after day after
day.
Send out your pigeons, Dai, send them out
With words of your anger and your love and your pride,
With stern little sentences wrought in your heart,
Send out your pigeons, flashing and dazzling towards the sun.

Go out, pigeons bach, and do what Dai tells you.

IDRIS DAVIES

138 The Gresford Disaster

You've heard of the Gresford disaster,
The terrible price that was paid;
Two hundred and forty-two colliers were lost
And three men of a rescue brigade.

It occurred in the month of September;
At three in the morning that pit
Was wracked by a violent explosion
In the Dennis where dust lay so thick.

The gas in the Dennis deep section
Was packed like snow in a drift,
And many a man had to leave the coal-face
Before he had worked out his shift.

A fornight before the explosion
To the shot-firer, Tomlinson cried:
'If you fire that shot we'll be all blown to hell!'
And no one can say that he lied.

The fireman's reports they are missing,
The records of forty-two days,
The colliery manager had them destroyed
To cover his criminal ways.

Down there in the dark they are lying,
They died for nine shillings a day;
They've worked out their shift and it's now they must lie
In the darkness until Judgement Day.

The Lord Mayor of London's collecting
To help both the children and wives.
The owners have sent some white lilies
To pay for the colliers' lives.

Farewell our dear wives and our children,
Farewell our dear comrades as well.
Don't send your sons in the dark dreary mine
They'll be damned like the sinners in Hell.

ANONYMOUS

139 Durham Gaol

You'll all have heard of Durham Gaol
But it would you much surprise
To see the prisoners in the yard
When they're on exercise.
The yard is built around with walls
So noble and so strong
Whoever goes there has to bide
Their time, be it short or long.

There's no good luck in Durham Gaol,
There's no good luck at all:
watery porridge   What is bread and skilly for?
Just to make you small.

When you go to Durham Gaol
They'll find you with employ,
They'll dress you up so dandy
In a suit of cordyroy,
They'll fetch a cap without a peak
And never ask your size
And like your suit it's cordyroy
And comes down o'er your eyes.

The first month is the worst of all,
Your feelings they will try;
There's nought but two great lumps of wood
On which you have to lie.
Then after that you get a bed
But it is hard as stones;
At night you daresn't make a turn
For fear you break some bones.

All kinds of work there's going on,
Upon them noble flats:
Teasing oakum, making balls
And weaving coco mats.
When you go in you may be thin
But they can make you thinner;
If your oakum isn't teased,
They're sure to stop your dinner.

The shoes you get is often tens,
The smallest size is nine;
They're big enough to make a skiff
For Boyd upon the Tyne!
And if you should be cold at nights,
Just make yourselves at home;
Lap your clothes around your shoes
And get inside of them!

THOMAS ARMSTRONG

140 A New Song on the Birth of the Prince of Wales

Who was Born on Tuesday, 9 November 1841

There's a pretty fuss and bother both in country and in town,
Since we have got a present, and an heir unto the Crown,
A little Prince of Wales so charming and so sly,
And the ladies shout with wonder, What a pretty little boy!

He must have a little musket, a trumpet and a kite,
A little penny rattle, and silver sword so bright,
A little cap and feather with scarlet coat so smart,
And a pretty little hobby horse to ride about the park.

Prince Albert he will often take the young Prince on his lap,
And fondle him so lovingly while he stirs about the pap,
He will pin on his flannel before he takes his nap,
Then dress him out so stylish with his little clouts and cap.

He must have a dandy suit to strut about the town,
John Bull must rake together six or seven thousand pound,
You'd laugh to see his daddy, at night he homewards runs,
With some peppermint or lollipops, sweet cakes and sugar
    plums.

He will want a little fiddle, and a little German flute,
A little pair of stockings and a pretty pair of boots,
With a handsome pair of spurs, and a golden headed cane,
And a stick of barley sugar, as long as Drury Lane.

An old maid ran through the palace, which did the nobs
   surprize,
Bawling out, he's got his daddy's mouth, his mammy's nose
   and eyes,
He would be as like his daddy as a frigate to a ship,
If he'd only got mustachios upon his upper lip.

Now to get these little niceties the taxes must be rose,
For the little Prince of Wales wants so many suits of clothes,
So they must tax the frying pan, the windows and the doors,
The bedsteads and the tables, kitchen pokers, and the floors.

ANONYMOUS

141 Surgeons must be Very Careful

Surgeons must be very careful
When they take the knife!
Underneath their fine incisions
Stirs the Culprit – *Life!*

EMILY DICKINSON

142 Earth Walks on Earth

Earth walks on Earth like glittering Gold;
Earth says to Earth, all's made of mould;
Earth builds on Earth, Castle and Towers,
Earth says to Earth, all shall be Ours.

TRADITIONAL

143 Mortality

Grass of levity,
Span in brevity,
Flowers' felicity,
Fire of misery,
Wind's stability,
Is mortality.

ANONYMOUS

144 Lines Before Execution

My prime of youth is but a frost of cares;
My feast of joy is but a dish of pain;
My crop of corn is but a field of tares;
And all my good is but vain hope of gain:
    The day is fled, and yet I saw no sun;
    And now I live, and now my life is done!

The spring is past, and yet it hath not sprung;
The fruit is dead, and yet the leaves are green;
My youth is gone, and yet I am but young;
I saw the world, and yet I was not seen:
    My thread is cut, and yet it is not spun;
    And now I live, and now my life is done!

I sought my death, and found it in my womb;
I looked for life, and saw it was a shade;
I trod the earth, and knew it was my tomb;
And now I die, and now I am but made:
    The glass is full, and now my glass is run;
    And now I live, and now my life is done!

CHIDIOCK TYCHBORN

145 Jerusalem, My Happy Home

Jerusalem, my happy home,
    When shall I come to thee?
When shall my sorrows have an end;
    Thy joys when shall I see?

O happy harbour of the saints,
    O sweet and pleasant soil,
In thee no sorrow may be found,
    No grief, no care, no toil.

There lust and lucre cannot dwell,
    There envy bears no sway;
There is no hunger, heat, nor cold,
    But pleasure every way.

Thy walls are made of precious stones,
  Thy bulwarks diamonds square;
Thy gates are of right orient pearl,
  Exceeding rich and rare.

Thy turrets and thy pinnacles
  With carbuncles do shine;
Thy very streets are paved with gold,
  Surpassing clear and fine.

Ah, my sweet home, Jerusalem,
  Would God I were in thee!
Would God my woes were at an end,
  Thy joys that I might see!

Thy gardens and thy gallant walks
  Continually are green;
There grows such sweet and pleasant flowers
  As nowhere else are seen.

Quite through the streets, with silver sound,
  The flood of life doth flow;
Upon whose banks on every side
  The wood of life doth grow.

There trees for evermore bear fruit,
  And evermore do spring;
There evermore the angels sit,
  And evermore do sing.

Our Lady sings Magnificat
  With tune surpassing sweet;
And all the virgins bear their part,
  Sitting about her feet.

Jerusalem, my happy home,
  Would God I were in thee!
Would God my woes were at an end,
  Thy joys that I might see!

ANONYMOUS

146 Epitaph to the Memory of
Captain Henry Clark

Our worthy friend who lies beneath this stone
Was master of a vessel all his own.
Houses and land had he and gold in store
He spent the whole and would if ten times more.

For twenty years he scarce slept in a bed,
sheds Linhays and limekilns lull'd his weary head
Because he would not to the Poor House go
For his proud spirit would not let him to.

The Blackbirds whistling notes at break of day
Used to awake him from his Bed of Hay.
Unto the Bridge and Quay he then repaired
To see what shipping up the river steered.

Oft in the week he used to view the bay
To see what Ships were coming in from sea.
To Captains' wives he brought the welcome news
And to the relatives of all their crews.

At last poor Harry Clark was taken ill
And carried to the workhouse 'gainst his will
But being of this mortal life quite tired
He lived about a month and then expired.

ANONYMOUS

147 Ship-Wrack

He, who has suffer'd Ship-wrack, fears to saile
Upon the Seas, though with a gentle gale.

ROBERT HERRICK

148 The Choirmaster's Burial

He often would ask us
That, when he died,
After playing so many
To their last rest,
If out of us any
Should here abide,
And it would not task us,
We would with our lutes
Play over him
By his grave-brim
The psalm he liked best –
The one whose sense suits
'Mount Ephraim' –
And perhaps we should seem
To him, in Death's dream,
Like the seraphim.

As soon as I knew
That his spirit was gone
I thought this his due,
And spake thereupon.
'I think,' said the vicar,
'A read service quicker
Than viols out-of-doors
In these frosts and hoars.
That old-fashioned way
Requires a fine day,
And it seems to me
It had better not be.'

Hence, that afternoon,
Though never knew he
That his wish could not be,
To get through it faster
They buried the master
Without any tune.

But 'twas said that, when
At the dead of next night
The vicar looked out,
There struck on his ken
Thronged roundabout,
Where the frost was graying
The headstoned grass,
A band all in white
Like the saints in church-glass,
Singing and playing
The ancient stave
By the choirmaster's grave.

Such the tenor man told
When he had grown old.

THOMAS HARDY

149 Flower Dump

tropical plants

Cannas shiny as slag,
Slug-soft stems,
Whole beds of bloom pitched on a pile,
Carnations, verbenas, cosmos,
Moulds, weeds, dead leaves,
Turned-over roots
With bleached veins
Twined like fine hair,
Each clump in the shape of a pot;
Everything limp
But one tulip on top,
One swaggering head
Over the dying, the newly dead.

THEODORE ROETHKE

150 Exeunt

Piecemeal the summer dies;
At the field's edge a daisy lives alone;
A last shawl of burning lies
On a gray field-stone.

All cries are thin and terse;
The field has droned the summer's final mass;
A cricket like a dwindled hearse
Crawls from the dry grass.

RICHARD WILBUR

151 A Lyke-Wake Dirge

Corpse Watch

This ae night, this ae night,
Every night and all,
Fire, and fleet, and candle-light,
And Christ receive thy soul.

When thou from hence away art passed,
Every night and all,
To Whinny-muir thou comest at last,
And Christ receive thy soul.

If ever thou gavest hosen and shoon,
Every night and all,
Sit thee down and put them on,
And Christ receive thy soul.

If hosen and shoon thou ne'er gavest nane,
Every night and all,
furze *or* gorse   The whinnes shall prick thee to the bare bane,
And Christ receive thy soul.

From Whinny-muir when thou mayest pass,
Every night and all,
bridge   To Brig o' Dread thou comest at last
And Christ receive thy soul.

From Brig o' Dread when thou mayest pass,
　　Every night and all,
To purgatory fire thou comest at last
　　And Christ receive thy soul.

If ever thou gavest meat or drink,
　　Every night and all,
The fire shall never make thee shrink
　　And Christ receive thy soul.

If meat or drink thou ne'er gavest nane,
　　Every night and all,
The fire will burn thee to the bare bane,
　　And Christ receive thy soul.

This ae night, this ae night,
　　Every night and all,
Fire, and fleet, and candle-light,
　　And Christ receive thy soul.

TRADITIONAL

152 Guilty

Dog draw. Stable stand.
Back berand. Bloody hand.

TRADITIONAL

That is, (1) holding a dog in leash, (2) standing concealed
with bow ready drawn, (3) detected carrying off a dead deer,
(4) the hands stained with blood, guilty – of poaching.

153 Finnegan's Wake

Tim Finnegan liv'd in Walkin Street,
A gentleman Irish mighty odd.
He had a tongue both rich and sweet,
An' to rise in the world he carried a hod,
Now Tim had a sort of a tipplin' way
With the love of the liquor he was born,
An' to help him on with his work each day,
creature He'd a drop of the craythur ev'ry morn.
    Whack fol the dah, dance to your partner,
    Welt the flure, yer trotters shake,
    Wasn't it the truth I told you,
    Lots of fun at Finnegan's Wake.

One morning Tim was rather full,
His head felt heavy which made him shake,
He fell from the ladder and broke his skull,
watch over So they carried him home his corpse to wake,
They rolled him up in a nice clean sheet,
And laid him out upon the bed,
With a gallon of whisky at his feet,
And a barrel of porter at his head.

His friends assembled at the wake,
And Mrs Finnegan called for lunch,
First they brought in tay and cake,
Then pipes, tobacco, and whiskey punch.
Miss Biddy O'Brien began to cry,
'Such a neat clean corpse, did you ever see,
Arrah, Tim ovourneen, why did you die?'
'Ah, hould your gab,' said Paddy McGee.

Then Biddy O'Connor took up the job,
'Biddy,' says she, 'you're wrong, I'm sure,'
But Biddy gave her a belt in the gob,
And left her sprawling on the floor;
Oh, then the war did soon enrage;
'Twas woman to woman and man to man,
Shillelagh law did all engage,
And a row and a ruction soon began.

Then Mickey Maloney raised his head,
When a noggin of whiskey flew at him,
It missed and falling on the bed,
The liquor scattered over Tim;
Bedad he revives, see how he rises,
And Timothy rising from the bed,
Says, 'Whirl your liquor round like blazes,
Thanam o'n dhoul, do ye think I'm dead?'
        Whack fol the dah, dance to your partner,
        Welt the flure, yer trotters shake,
        Wasn't it the truth I told you,
        Lots of fun at Finnegan's Wake.

TRADITIONAL

154   Reader, Pass On

Reader, pass on, nor waste your precious time
On bad biography and murdered rhyme;
What I was before's well known to my neighbours
What I am now is no concern of yours.

ANONYMOUS

155   The Twa Corbies

As I was walking all alane,
^{ravens} I heard twa corbies making a mane:
The tane unto the tither did say,
'Whar sall we gang and dine the day?'

^{turf} 'In behint yon auld fail dyke
I wot there lies a new-slain knight;
And naebody kens that he lies there
But his hawk, his hound, and his lady fair.

His hound is to the hunting gane,
His hawk to fetch the wild-fowl hame,
His lady's ta'en anither mate,
So we may mak' our dinner sweet.

neck   Ye'll sit on his white hause-bane,
And I'll pike out his bonny e'en:
Wi' ae lock o' his gowden hair
thatch   We'll theek our nest when it grows bare.

Many a one for him maks mane,
But nane sall ken whar he is gane:
O'er his white banes, when they are bare,
The wind sall blaw for evermair.'

TRADITIONAL

156 The Three Ravens

There were three ravens sat on a tree,
   Down a down, hay down, hay down,
There were three ravens sat on a tree,
   With a down,
There were three ravens sat on a tree,
They were as black as they might be,
   With a down derrie, derrie, derrie, down, down.

The one of them said to his mate,
'Where shall we our breakfast take?

'Down in yonder green field,
There lies a knight slain under his shield.

'His hounds they lie down at his feet,
So well they can their master keep.

'His hauks they flie so eagerly,
There's no fowl dare him come nie.'

Down there comes a fallow doe,
As great with yong as she might goe.

She lifted up his bloudy hed,
And kist his wounds that were so red.

She got him up upon her back,
And carried him to earthen lake.

She buried him before the prime,
She was dead herself ere even-song time.

God send every gentleman
lover   Such hauks, such hounds, and such a leman.

ANONYMOUS

157   Epitaph

Here lies, in horizontal position
    the outside case of
G EORGE R OUTLEIGH, Watchmaker ;
Whose abilities in that line were an honour
    to his profession,
Integrity was the Mainspring, and prudence the
    Regulator
    of all the actions of his life.
Humane, generous and liberal,
    His Hand never stopped
    till he had relieved distress.
So nicely regulated were all his motions,
    that he never went wrong,
    except when set a-going
    by people
who did not know his Key ;
    even then he was easily
    set right again.
He had the art of disposing his time so well,
    that his hours glided away
    in one continual round
    of pleasure and delight,
Until an unlucky minute put a period to
    his existence.
    He departed this life
    Nov. 14, 1802 :
    aged 57 :
    wound up,
    In hopes of being taken in hand
    by his Maker ;
And of being thoroughly cleaned, repaired,
    and set a-going
    In the world to come.

ANONYMOUS

158 The Spiritual Railway

The Line to Heaven by Christ was made,
With heavenly truth the Rails were laid,
From Earth to Heaven the Line extends,
To Life Eternal where it ends.
Repentance is the Station then,
Where Passengers are taken in,
No FEE for them is there to pay,
For Jesus is himself the way.
God's Word is the First Engineer,
It points the way to Heaven so clear.
Through tunnels dark and dreary here,
It does the way to Glory steer.
God's Love the Fire, his Truth the Steam,
Which drives the Engine and the Train.
All you who would to Glory ride,
Must come to Christ, in him abide.
In First, and Second, and Third Class,
Repentance, Faith and Holiness,
You must the way to Glory gain,
Or you with Christ will not remain.
Come then, poor Sinners, now's the time,
At any station on the Line,
If you'll repent and turn from sin,
The Train will stop and take you in.

ANONYMOUS

159 On John Pye, a Farmer

Here lies *John Pye!*
  Oh! oh!
  Does he so?
There let him lye.

ANONYMOUS

160   On Mr Foote

Here lies one FOOTE, whose death may thousands save,
For death has now one FOOTE within the grave.

ANONYMOUS

161   'Biby's' Epitaph

A muvver was barfin' 'er biby one night,
The youngest of ten and a tiny young mite,
The muvver was poor and the biby was thin,
Only a skelington covered in skin;
The muvver turned rahnd for the soap off the rack,
She was but a moment, but when she turned back,
The biby was gorn; and in anguish she cried,
'Oh, where is my biby?' – The angels replied:

'Your biby 'as fell dahn the plug-'ole,
Your biby 'as gorn dahn the plug;
The poor little thing was so skinny and thin
'E oughter been barfed in a jug;
Your biby is perfeckly 'appy,
'E won't need a barf any more,
Your biby 'as fell dahn the plug-'ole,
Not lorst, but gorn before.'

ANONYMOUS

162   An Epitaph at Great Torrington, Devon

Here lies a man who was killed by lightning;
He died when his prospects seemed to be brightening.
He might have cut a flash in this world of trouble,
But the flash cut him, and he lies in the stubble.

ANONYMOUS

163 The American Indian

There once were some people called Sioux
Who spent all their time making shioux
Which they coloured in various hioux ;
Don't think that they made them to ioux
Oh ! no, they just sold them for bioux.

ANONYMOUS

164 The Shades of Night

The shades of night were falling fast
And the rain was falling faster
When through an Alpine village passed
An Alpine village pastor.

A. E. HOUSMAN

165 That's All

There was an old man,
And he had a calf,
  And that's half.
He took him out of the stall
And put him on the wall,
  And that's all.

TRADITIONAL

166 From 'The Shepherd's Calendar, December'

The shepherd now no more afraid
Since custom doth the chance bestow
Starts up to kiss the giggling maid
Beneath the branch of mizzletoe
That neath each cottage beam is seen
Wi pearl-like berrys shining gay
The shadow still of what hath been
Which fashion yearly fades away

And singers too a merry throng
At early morn wi simple skill
Yet imitate the angels song
And chant their christmass ditty still
And mid the storm that dies and swells
By fits – in humings softly steals
The music of the village bells
Ringing round their merry peals

And when its past a merry crew
Bedeckt in masks and ribbons gay
The 'Morrice danse' their sports renew
And act their winter evening play
The clown-turnd-kings for penny praise
Storm wi the actors strut and swell
And harlequin a laugh to raise
Wears his hump back and tinkling bell

And oft for pence and spicy ale
Wi winter nosgays pind before
The wassail singer tells her tale
And drawls her christmass carrols oer
The prentice boy wi ruddy face
rime   And ryhme bepowderd dancing locks
From door to door wi happy pace
Runs round to claim his 'christmass box'

JOHN CLARE

167 Christmas Mummer's Play

Song begins outside. Then Mummers dance in singing:
as they come in they form a circle. Each has his sword
over his right shoulder and the man behind takes hold
of the sword of the man in front of him. The Fool comes
behind the tallest man and pretends that he cannot reach
his sword-point – plays the fool with it. Song ended they
stand back and *At Once* Enter Father Christmas, who walks
forward and then round in a ring.

FATHER CHRISTMAS
Here come I, Old Father Christmas.
Welcome or welcome not
I hope Old Father Christmas
Will never be forgot.
My head is white, my back is bent,
My knees are weak, my strength is spent.
Nineteen hundred and sixty —
Is a very great age for me.
And if I had been growing all these years
What a monster I should be.

FOOL
An old man indeed thou must be,
And thou seemest but three score and three.

FATHER CHRISTMAS
(Pushing Fool aside)
A room, a room, a gallant room,
And give us room to rhyme,
We've come to show activity
Upon this Christmas time.
Acting youth or acting age,
The like was never seen upon this stage.
(Stands back)

FOOL
Room, room, brave gallants, give us room to sport.
For to this room we wish now to resort.
(Swings bladder at audience and performers)

(Enter Sweep)
SWEEP
Sweep, sweep a room for me
And all our jolly company.
Sweep, sweep, – a sweep am I
Will sweep for one and all right merrily.

(Sings) Oh, my name it is Jack Hall, chimney sweep,
Oh, my name it is Jack Hall, chimney sweep,
Oh, my name it is Jack Hall, and I've robbed both great and
  small,
And my neck shall pay for all when I die, when I die.

I have twenty pound in store, that's no joke,
I have twenty pound in store, that's no joke,
I have twenty pound in store, and I'll rob for twenty more,
And my neck shall pay for all when I die, when I die.

Oh they tell me that in jail I shall die,
Oh they tell me that in jail I shall die,
Oh they tell me that in jail I shall drink no more brown ale.
And my neck shall pay for all when I die, when I die.

Up the ladder I did grope, that's no joke,
Up the ladder I did grope, that's no joke,
Up the ladder I did grope, and the hangman spread the rope.
Oh, but never a word said I coming down, coming down.

FOOL   Come, come, thou sweep,
        Enough of thee.
        (Enter St George for all to see)
        Now St George, thou champion bold,
        Thou has fought much as I've been told.
        If that be true, pray tell us now
        Where thou hast fought, and when, and how?

ST GEORGE   *(Swaggers round)*
        Here comes I, St George, the valiant man,
        With my broad sword and spear in hand,
        Who fought the Dragon and brought him to the slaughter,
        And for this won the King of Egypt's daughter.
        What man or mortal before me dares to stand
        I'll cut him down with this deadly hand.
        I'll slay him and cut him as small as flies
        And send him to Jamaica to make mince pies.

        (Enter Turkish Knight, who should be as tall as possible)
TURKISH   Here come I, the Turkish Knight,
KNIGHT   In Turkish Land I learnt to fight.

I'll fight St George with courage bold
And if his blood is hot, I'll run it cold.
(Fiercely as possible)

ST GEORGE Tut, tut, thou little fellow!
Thy talk is very bold ;
Just like those little Turks
As I've been told.
If thou be a Turkish Knight
Pull out thy sword and fight!
Or pull out thy purse and pay
For I'll have satisfaction
Before I go away.

TURKISH St George, St George! Thou dost not well to boast.
KNIGHT The Knight of Turkey is my name,
And by my sharp sword at my side
I hope to win the game.
My body's lined with lead,
My head is made of steel,
So to battle, to battle, let thee and I try
To see which on the ground shall lie.
(They fight furiously. Onlookers cheer, some one, some the other. The Turkish Knight falls)

ST GEORGE O Ladies and Gentlemens, you see what I have done,
I've struck this Turk down like the Evening Sun!

FATHER Fear not, I have a little bottle by me side,
CHRISTMAS In it hocum, slocum, a liquid spar,
I'll touch his eyes, nose, mouth, and chin,
And say 'Rise, dead man' and he'll fight again.
(Turk leaps up ready to fight, and they go at it again, even more furiously. Turk again falls, and lies quite stiff)

(Enter Moll Finney)
MOLL St George, St George, what has thou done?
Thou has surely ruined thyself
By killing my only son. *(Kneels beside Turk)*
Is there a doctor to be found
Can cure a man lies bleeding on the ground?

FOOL   *(Running round)*
        Doctor, doctor, come and see,
        This man is wounded in the knee.
        Doctor, doctor, come and try,
        This man is wounded in the thigh.
        Doctor, doctor, do thy part,
        This man is wounded in the heart.

        (Enter Doctor)
DOCTOR I be the noble Doctor Good.
        And with my skill I'll stop his blood;
        My fee's *ten* pound, but only *five* if I
        Don't raise this man alive.

FOOL   What canst do then, Doctor?

MOLL   Doctor, doctor, cure this man.

DOCTOR No. I see he's too far gone

MOLL   *(weeping)* Then walk in, Jack Vinney.

        (Enter Jack Vinney to left of body)
JACK VINNEY My name is not Jack Vinney,
        My name is Mr John Vinney,
        A man of fame,
        Come from Spain,
        Do more than any man again.

DOCTOR What canst thou do, Jack?

JACK VINNEY Cure a magpie with the toothache.

FOOL   How do that then, Doctor?

DOCTOR Cut his head off and throw his body in the ditch. –
        Any fool could do that.

JACK VINNEY Thou callst me a Fool, dost thou?

FOOL   Now cheer up, Jack, don't get thee crusty.

JACK VINNEY Take care you Fool, or I'll chop thee as fine as dust,
        And send thee to make mince-pie crust.

DOCTOR   *(Drags Fool away, and signs Jack to the body)*
          Now, Jack, cure this man.

JACK VINNEY   Give me my spectacles.
               (He is handed a huge pair of wooden spectacles)
               Now give me my pliars.
               (He is handed great pliars – makes great to-do and finally produces a huge horse's tooth)
               Here's a tooth enough to kill any man
               But he will cure this man.
               (Turk is pulled up and shakes Jack's hand)

JACK VINNEY   I come from Spain,
               Thou comes from France,
               Call in the Morris Men,
               Let's have a dance.
               (Morris men come forward and dance 'Shepherd's Hey' with crossed swords. When this is over, St George and Turkish Knight come forward)

TURKISH KNIGHT	St George, St George, pardon me, pardon me,
	And from this country give me leave to flee.

ST GEORGE   Go home. Go home. Thou curly Turkish Knight,
Go back to thine own land
And learn to fight :
Tell them all across the sea
We'll fight a thousand men like thee.

FOOL   St George, thou speakest very bold,
And hast good cause as I've been told.

ST GEORGE   Here am I, St George, in shining armour bright,
I am a famous champion,
Likewise a worthy knight :
Seven long years in a close cave was kept,
And out of that into a prison leapt.
Many a giant did I subdue
And fought the fiery dragon too.
First I fought in France
Second I fought in Spain
And now I've come to Kempsford[1]
The Dragon to fight again.
(Stands back to right)

DRAGON   Stand on head, stand on feet,
Meat, meat, meat, for to eat !

I am the Dragon, here are my jaws
I am the Dragon, here are my claws.
Meat, meat, meat, for to eat,

Stand on head, stand on feet.
(Snaps at all performers, who draw back in terror)

FOOL   *(Dodges to side of St George)*
Now champion bold knocked down the Turkish Knight,
Make haste to kill the dragon in the fight.

ST GEORGE   Should twenty thousand Dragons rise,
I'd fight them all before your eyes.
And now I'll slay the Dragon – my wonders to begin,
A fell and fiery dragon he, but I will clip his wing.
(They fight, onlookers cheer them on. St George falls. Right Hand, St George's man, rushes to help and supports him against his knee)

1. Or wherever you are performing the play.

RIGHT HAND	Alack, alack, my master he has slain, Send tell the doctor he must come again.
DOCTOR	Here come I, the Doctor Good, I'll stop the noble Champion's blood.
RIGHT HAND	Pray, Doctor, where do you come from?
DOCTOR	I come from Portugal, France, and Spain, To fetch dead people to life again.
RIGHT HAND	Pray, noble doctor, what can you cure?
DOCTOR	I have some pills To cure all ills, Hard corns, soft corns, any corns that be, The itch, the stitch, the palsy and the gout, Pains within and pains without, And any old woman that's been dead seven year, If she's got one tooth left to crack one of these here. (*Holds up box and shakes it to rattle the pills, finally opens it, takes out a huge pill and stuffs it into St George's mouth*)
DOCTOR	Rise up, St George, and fight again And may the Dragon yet be slain (*They fight again – at last Dragon falls dead*)
ST GEORGE	(*Exhausted but triumphant, on one knee*) Now I have killed the Dragon and brought him to the slaughter.
FOOL	(*Pretending to hunt for someone*) Alas, where is the King of Egypt's daughter?
ST GEORGE	Long ago she died and lies at rest But still I fight to succour the opprest.
FATHER CHRISTMAS	St George, thou hast the Dragon slain again, With thy brave hand his life is nobly ta'en.
TANNER	Away from here his body carry fast First go his feet and then his head come last.

ALL   Which is his head? Is this it? Is that it?
       (Dragon carried out feet first)

       (Enter Big Head)
BIG HEAD   In comes I, as ha'n't been hit
       With my big head, and little wit,
       My head's so big and my wit's so small,
       Come in Humpty Jack to please them all.
       (Some of the actors dance 'Bacca Pipe's Jig' over swords)

       (Enter Beelzebub)
BEELZEBUB   In comes I, Beelzebub,
       In my hand I carries a club;
       And in my hand a warming pan.
       And don't you think
       I'm a merry old man?

       (Enter Humpty Jack)
HUMPTY JACK   Here comes I, little Humpty Jack,
       Wife and family on my back
       Out of nine I haven't but five.
       And half of them are starved alive.
       The roads are dirty and our shoes are bad.
       So please put *something* into our bag,
       Ladies and Gents our play is ended
       Our money box is recommended.

       Beelzebub goes round with the box while other actors sing
       'Good King Wenceslas'. Morris off, with Dragon too, to
       'Maid o' the Mill'. Twice round room and out, Fool coming
       last, fooling to the end.

       ANONYMOUS

168 F for Fig

F for fig,
I for jig, and
N for Knuckley Boney,
I for John the waterman, and
S for Sarah Stoney.

ANONYMOUS

Tunes for Some Poems

47 **Ground-Hog**

Whet up yer knife and whi - stle up yer dogs,

Whet up yer knife and whi - stle up yer dogs, A - way to the hills to

repeats   end

catch ground-hogs, GROUND-HOG!

49 **Old Blue**

I had an ol' dog, boys—, and I called him

Blue, Lis - ten lem - me tell you what Blue could do.

Come on, Blue—, you good dog, you, Yes—, come on, Blue—,

end

you good dog, you.

101   **Scarborough Fair**

Are you go - ing to Scar - bo - rough Fair — ?

Pars - ley, Sage —, Rose - ma - ry and Thyme-

Re - mem - ber me— to one who lived

there—, For once she was— a true love of mine.

106   **I Once Went A-Courting**

I once went a - cour - ting an old wo - man's daugh - ter. She

quick - ly found out what us young 'uns was af - ter. With

arms stuck a - kim - bo in quar - rel - some mood, She

swore that she'd set - tle our loves if she could.

Down, down der - ry down day.

In— No - ro - way— there—

sits a maid—: 'By - loo, my ba - by—,'

she be - gins— 'Lit - tle know

I my— child's— fa - ther—, Or if
top line vv. 3, 5 and 8

land— or— sea— he's—

last
verse (8)

liv - ing in.'

127 **John Randall**

Where— have you been to, John Ran - dall my son—? Where— have you been to, my hand - some young man—? A hawk - ing and hunt - ing; moth - er, make my bed soon—: I'm sick at my heart and I fain— would lie— down—

136 **On a British Submarine**

It hap - pened on a sun - ny day in nine - teen fif - ty four. We went to greet Her Maj - es - ty a - com - ing from the tour. On a Brit - ish sub - ma - rine, on a Brit - ish sub - ma - rine, When six - ty so - lid sail - ors went a - cheer - ing of the Queen.

138 The Gresford Disaster

You've heard of the Gres-ford dis-as-ter, The ter-ri-ble price that was paid—; Two hun-dred and for-ty-two col-liers were lost And three men of a res-cue bri-gade—.

139 Durham Gaol

You'll all have heard of Dur-ham Gaol But it
sim. sempre
would you much sur-prise— To see the pri-son-ers in the yard When they're on ex-er-cise— The yard is built a-round with walls So no-ble and so strong-- Who-ev-er goes there to

bide their time—, Be it short or

sim.

long—. O there's no good luck in Dur - ham Gaol, There's

no good luck at all—: What's bread and

skil - ly for? But just to make you small.

151   A Lyke-Wake Dirge

This ae night, this ae night, Ev - er - y night and all,

Fire, and fleet, and can - dle - light—, And Christ re - ceive thy soul.

155   The Twa Corbies

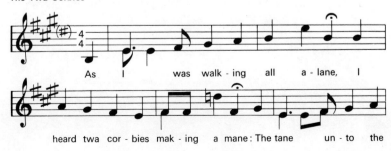

As I was walk - ing all a - lane, I

heard twa cor - bies mak - ing a mane: The tane un - to the

ti - ther did say, 'Whar sall we gang and dine the—
day—? Whar— sall we gang and dine the— day—?'

156   The Three Ravens

There were three ra - vens sat on a tree,

Down a down, hay down, hay down They were as black as

they might be, With a down, The one of them said

to his mate, 'Where shall we our break - fast take? With a

down der - rie, der - rie, der - rie, down —, down.

repeat

last verse

A muv - ver was bar - fin' 'er bi - by one night, The
The muv - ver turned rahnd for the soap off the rack, She

youn - gest of ten and a ti - ny young mite, The
was but a mo - ment, but when she turned back, The

muv - ver was poor and the bi - by was thin—, 'Oh,
bi - by was gorn; and in an - guish she cried,

On - ly 'a skel - ing - ton cov - ered in skin; Your
where is my bi - by?' The an - gels re - plied: Your

bi - by as fell dahn the plug 'ole, Your bi - by 'as
bi - by is per - feck - ly 'ap - py, 'E won't need a

gorn dahn the plug; The poor lit - tle thing was so
barf a - ny more, Your bi - by 'as fell dahn the

1st time

skin - ny and thin 'E ought - er been barfed in a jug—;
plug 'ole,

2nd time

Not lorst, but gorn be - fore, Not lorst, but gorn be - fore.'

Acknowledgements

For permission to use copyright material acknowledgement is made to the following:

Poems For 104 to W. H. Auden and Faber and Faber Ltd; for 32 from *Poems* by Elizabeth Bishop to Elizabeth Bishop and Chatto and Windus Ltd; for 40 from *A Beachcomber's Diary* by John Blight to John Blight and Angus and Robertson Ltd; for 46 to Ronald Bottrall; for 114 to Nancy Cato Norman; for 13, 76, 103, 108 and 126 to Charles Causley and David Higham Associates Ltd; for 23, 34, 98, 99, 100, 102, 127, 129 and 166 to Eric Robinson; for 137 to Faber and Faber Ltd; for 128 and 141, from Thomas H. Johnson (ed.), *The Poems of Emily Dickinson*, to the President and Fellows of Harvard College and Harvard University Press; for 58 to Faber and Faber Ltd; for 123 to the Pegasus Press Ltd; for 8, 71, 78, 115 and 125 from *Collected Poems 1959* by Robert Graves to Robert Graves; for 14, 50, 79 and 148 from *The Collected Poems of Thomas Hardy* to the Trustees of the Hardy Estate, the Macmillan Co. of Canada Ltd and Macmillan and Co. Ltd; for 4 to W. Hart Smith and the Caxton Press; for 6 and 37 to Faber and Faber Ltd; for the translation of 88 to Doubleday and Company Inc.; for 164 to the Estate of the late A. E. Housman and the Society of Authors; for 87 and 133 to Harrold Ober Associates; for 22 to Faber and Faber Ltd; for 130 from *The Lost World* by Randall Jarrell to Eyre and Spottiswoode Ltd; for 45 from *Double Axe and Other Poems* and 55 from *Hungerfield and Other Poems* by Robinson Jeffers to Random House Inc.; for 94 to M. K. Joseph; for 5 to Penguin Books Ltd; for 54 to Tom Langley and the Wolverhampton Folk Song Club; for 31, 53, 117 and 118 to Laurence Pollinger Ltd and the Estate of the late Mrs Frieda Lawrence; for 44 to New Directions Inc.; for 39 to Angus and Robertson Ltd; for 74 and 113 to R. A. K. Mason and The Caxton Press; for 77 to Ray Mathew; for 73 from *Poems* by Archibald McLeish to Archibald McLeish and the Bodley Head; for 27, 38 and 43 from *The Colussus* by Sylvia Plath to Ted Hughes and Faber and Faber Ltd; for 116 to the Macmillan Co. of New York; for 121 and 149 to Faber and Faber Ltd; for 72 and 131 from *The Collected Poems of Isaac Rosenberg* to the Literary Estate of Isaac Rosenberg and Chatto and Windus Ltd; for 107 to Justin St John; for 30, 93 and 135 from *Smoke and Steel* and for 80 from *Good Morning, America* by Carl Sandburg to Harcourt, Brace and World Inc.; for 12 to Vernon Scannell; for 63 from *Good News of Death and Other Poems* by Louis Simpson to Charles Scribner's Sons Inc.; for 60 to Angus and Robertson Ltd; for 51 from *Travelling Through the Dark* and for 75 from *The Rescued Year* by William Stafford to Harper and Row Publishers Inc.; for 25, 112 and 120 from *Out of Bounds* by Jon Stallworthy to Oxford University Press; for 36, which first appeared in *The New Yorker*, from *To Mix with Time* by May Swenson to Charles Scribner's Sons Inc.; for 136 to Cyril Tawney and Folk Directions (Publishing) Ltd; for 26 and 111 to Mrs Myfanwy Thomas; for 52 and 122 from *American Scenes and Other Poems* by Charles Tomlinson to Oxford University Press; for 3 to Indiana University Press; for 2, 9, 61, 62 and 82 from *Chinese Poems* translated by Arthur Waley to George Allen and Unwin Ltd; for 10 from *The Self-Made Man* and for 132 from *The Boy from Iowa* by Reed Whittemore to the Macmillan Co. of New York Inc.; for 11, 48, 64 and 150 to Faber and Faber Ltd; for 68 from *Collected Earlier Poems* and for 96 and 119 from *Pictures from Brueghel* by William Carlos Williams to MacGibbon and Kee Ltd.

Pictures For the pictures on pages 8–9, 135 and 139 to James Hogg; pages 18, 63, 91 and 95 to Roger Mayne; page 22 to W. E. R. Hallgarth; page 27 to the Museo del Prado, Madrid; page 35 to Bridget Riley and the Trustees of the Tate Gallery; page 55, from Gordon Winter, *A Country Camera*, Country Life, 1967, to Country Life Ltd; page 70 to the Imperial War Museum; pages 98–9 and 103 to the Stadelschen Kunstinstitut, Frankfurt am Main; page 124 to Lawrence Darton; page 143 to the United States Information Service, Paris; pages 152–3 to the Kunsthistorische Museum, Vienna; page 163 to Bill Brandt; page 171 to the Bedford County Record Office.

Every effort has been made to trace owners of copyright material, but in some cases this has not proved possible. The publishers would be glad to hear from any further copyright owners of material reproduced in *Voices*.

List of Illustrations

Index of Titles

Numbers refer to the numbers of poems

Index of First Lines

Numbers refer to the numbers of poems

The river was announcing, 123
The shades of night were falling fast, 164
The shepherd now no more afraid, 166
The snow came down last night like moths, 64
The Wind – tapped like a tired Man, 128
There dwelt a man in fair Westmoreland, 124
There is no one among men that has not a special failing, 2
There once were some people called Sioux, 163
There was a man with a tongue of wood, 1
There was an old man, 165
There were three ravens sat on a tree, 156
There's a pretty fuss and bother both in country and in town, 140
There's some that sing of the hiring fair, 16
They fought south of the Castle, 56
They hold their hands over their mouths, 3
They were calling certain styles of whiskers by the name of 'lilacs', 30
They're out of the dark's ragbag, these two, 27
This ae night, this ae night, 151
This Blatant Beast was finally overcome, 125
This face you got, 80
This girl, 94
This knot I knit, 89
This, quoth the Eskimo master, 74
Tim Finnegan liv'd in Walkin Street, 153
Timothy Winters comes to school, 76
Travelling through the dark I found a deer, 51
'Twas in the year two thousand and one, 65

'Underneath this hazelin mote', 42
Upon the collar of an hugh old oak, 23

Vlee away, blackie cap, 24

When did you start your tricks, 31
When I saw the fox, it was kneeling, 52
When I was a chicken as big as a hen, 83
When I wer still a bwoy, an' mother's pride, 70
When I wish I was rich, then I know I am ill, 117
When the mouse died, there was a sort of pity, 40
Where have you been to, John Randall my son?, 127
Whet up yer knife and whistle up yer dogs, 47
While gentlefolks strut in their silver and satins, 15
While in this cavernous place employed, 115
White hairs cover my temples, 82
Why flyest thou away with fear?, 28
'Why of the sheep do you not learn peace?', 67

You slapped my face, 96
You'll all have heard of Durham Gaol, 139
You've heard of the Gresford disaster, 138

Index of Poets, Translators and Collectors

Numbers refer to the numbers of poems